DESCENT INTO MADNESS:

AN INMATE'S EXPERIENCE OF THE NEW MEXICO STATE PRISON RIOT

BY MIKE ROLLAND

anderson publishing co.
2035 Reading Rd.
Cincinnati, OH 45202
1-800-582-7295

since 1887

Descent Into Madness:
An Inmate's Experience of the New Mexico State Prison Riot

ISBN 0-87084-748-1
Library of Congress Catalog Number 97-71307

Gail Eccleston *Editor*   *Acquisitions Editor* Michael Braswell

Cover design by Tin Box Studio/Cincinnati, OH
Cover photo credit: Guildhaus Photographics/Cincinnati, OH

. . . *Alone*

Through the depths of darkness
To the brightness of light
A man may walk alone.

Through the purification of his soul
To the rivers of his mind,
A man can make it alone...

Through wars and hate
To the madness of prison,
This man has been alone.

But will a tear come to your eye
When you see this foolish man die
Alone...

M. Rolland
3-14-72

This book is dedicated to my mother, Joyce H. Seabolt,
who always knew I would accomplish this goal.
1930-1987

—Mike Rolland

Acknowledgments

I want to thank Priscilla Maine for helping by staying after me to write this story. Wayne Brakensiek, for providing inspiration in moments of uncertainty. Julie T. Sandridge, for figuring out what I wanted to say and putting it in format. Also, I must thank my sister, Mary Ann R. Simmons, for believing in me when no one else could.

—Mike Rolland

Preface

by Michael Braswell*

Descent Into Madness provides a unique contribution to the literature. The book begins with an objective overview of the New Mexico State Prison riot by Mark Colvin, a sociologist who has studied the riot extensively. His introduction provides an academic framework from which to contrast the subjective, day-to-day account of surviving the riot by Mike Rolland, an inmate who lived through it. Colvin provides expertise, Rolland, the experience. In a brief epilogue, Bo Lozoff, who has worked with prison inmates for more than 20 years, offers a commentary on the condition of violence found in our prisons and challenges some fundamental assumptions concerning prisons and prisoners.

The heart and uniqueness of this book is the narrative account of the riot by Mike Rolland. The reader is immersed into the center of the experience that was the New Mexico State Prison riot. The experience is one of an extreme and tenuous existence; a place of darkness for inmates and hostages alike, where hope was small, and fear and despair were constants. I believe the importance of this narrative lies in its uncompromising description of the devastating consequences of what can go wrong in our system of justice. *Descent Into Madness* describes the worst that can happen—the end-of-the-line result when individually and collectively we look the other way and ignore the complexities and humanity of our criminal justice process. And implicit in that description is a warning: if we do not take better care, what happened there—to them—may also happen here, to us.

*   East Tennessee State University.

Table of Contents

PART I

Introduction

by Mark Colvin*

The riot at the Penitentiary of New Mexico (PNM) on February 2 and 3, 1980 is without parallel for its violence, destruction, and disorganization. During the 36 hours of the riot, 33 inmates were killed by other inmates; many of the victims were tortured and mutilated. (A 34th inmate died several months later from injuries he received during the riot.) As many as 200 inmates were severely injured from beatings, stabbings, and rapes. Many more suffered less serious injuries. In addition, scores of inmates were treated for overdoses of drugs taken from the prison's pharmacy during the riot. That more inmates did not die can be attributed to the dedicated work of medical personnel and emergency crews who treated the injured and transported them to local hospitals. In fact, many inmates were later surprised to learn of riot survivors whom they thought had certainly died during the event.

Seven of the 12 correctional officers who were taken hostage were beaten, stabbed, or sodomized. None of the hostages were killed. Some of the guard hostages were protected by small groups of inmates during the riot. A few hostages were even assisted in leaving the prison during the riot by sympathetic inmates.

Correctional officers and many more inmates would have certainly died in the riot had it not been for heroic efforts of some prisoners who risked their lives to save others from harm. Indeed, this prison riot brought out not only the evil potential of human beings (upon which we tend to focus after such an event) but also the poten-

---

* Mark Colvin is Associate Professor of Sociology at George Mason University, Fairfax, Virginia. In 1980, he was a principal researcher with the New Mexico Attorney General's official investigation of the events and causes of the 1980 riot at the Penitentiary of New Mexico. He had worked at the Penitentiary of New Mexico as an educational counselor and parole officer in 1975 and 1976, and as a corrections planner with the New Mexico Governor's Council on Criminal Justice Planning from 1976-1978. He completed a Ph.D. in sociology from the University of Colorado at Boulder in 1985. In 1992, he published *The Penitentiary in Crisis* (SUNY Press) which looks at the organizational history of the Penitentiary of New Mexico leading up to the riot. He has published articles on prisons, criminological theory, and criminal justice policies in several journals, including the *American Journal of Sociology, Social Problems, Sociological Quarterly,* and *Crime and Delinquency.* He is currently publishing a book on the history of penal practices in nineteenth-century America, titled *Penitentiaries, Reformatories, Chain Gangs.*

tial for virtue. We are quick to condemn the evil acts and use these as an excuse to label all prisoners as "animals." But to do so is to ignore the acts of kindness and courage displayed by many inmates; to ignore the fact that the overwhelming majority of inmates only wanted to escape the mayhem, the violence, and the fear; and to ignore the essential humanity of the great majority of the people we lock up in prisons. Focusing on the evil acts of those few prisoners who engaged in them also distracts us from the evil of a taxpayer-supported prison system that produces events like the New Mexico State Prison riot.

The riot caused $20 million in physical damage to the institution. Fires were started throughout the prison, and water flooded the prison water mains. More than $200 million in riot-related expenses were incurred by the state for medical, police, fire, and national guard response, lawsuits for injuries and wrongful death, transportation of inmates to federal and other state prison systems, prosecutions of crimes committed during the riot, and official investigations of the events and causes of the riot.

The official investigation of the riot was headed by then-Attorney General of New Mexico Jeff Bingaman. I was hired by the Attorney General as a principal researcher for the riot investigation. In that role, I, along with the riot investigation team, conducted more than 300 in-depth interviews with former and then-current prisoners, correctional officers, and corrections officials in an attempt to reconstruct the events of the riot and understand its long-term causes and effects. The riot investigation presented its findings and conclusions in a two-part report (Office of the Attorney General, 1980a,b). More recently, I published a book that presents a detailed social and organizational history of the Penitentiary of New Mexico State Prison leading up to this riot (Colvin, 1992). *Descent Into Madness* by Mike Rolland complements those other works by taking the reader inside a major prison riot. It is a gripping story that brings this event to life as experienced by someone who survived it. For this reason, it is an important book. While I cannot confirm every event reported in Mike Rolland's account, I can say, as someone who has studied this event very closely, that the account is authentic and accords on most points with the official version of events.

In this introduction, I hope to provide the reader with a context for understanding Mike Rolland's account of the New Mexico State Prison riot. It is important to understand the history of this prison, since it was not always a violent and disorderly institution. It was only in the three to four years preceding the riot that the prison had moved toward becoming the type of violent and disorganized organization that could produce an event as brutal as the 1980 riot. This introduction will also provide the reader with an overview of the riot itself, presenting the big picture of the event before the reader encounters Mike Rolland's close-up view of it.

Background of the Riot

The 1980 New Mexico State Prison riot stands in stark contrast to the 1971 Attica prison riot. At Attica, after a few hours of chaos and destruction in which three inmates were killed by other inmates, inmate leaders were able to take command of rioting inmates and turn the event into an organized protest about prison conditions; after that point, no other deaths occurred until state authorities violently retook the prison, killing 29 inmates and 10 guard hostages in the process (Wicker, 1975). At New Mexico, inmate leaders, to the extent that there were any, were unable to organize inmates or stop the inmate-on-inmate violence. All inmates were killed by other inmates. No one was killed when state authorities retook the prison. The disorganization of the riot and the inmate-on-inmate killings, and the brutality of many of these killings, are what distinguish the New Mexico State Prison riot.

As stated, the Penitentiary of New Mexico (PNM) was not always a violent, disorganized prison. In fact, on July 14, 1976, inmates at this prison staged a well-organized, peaceful protest of prison conditions. In the previous six months, a new prison administration had begun dismantling prison programs and reducing inmate privileges. The curtailment of programs and special privileges soon led to an open confrontation between the new prison administration and inmates. Prisoners organized a massive sit-down strike in which nearly 800 of the prison's 912 inmates refused to leave their living quarters for work or meals. The level of participation in this 1976 strike demonstrated a high degree of solidarity and cooperation among inmates. There was no violence among inmates during this event. (In fact, no inmate had been killed by another inmate at this prison since before 1970.) The prison administration's response to this June 1976 inmate strike inaugurated a new era in staff and inmate relations and in relations among inmates. It was a new era characterized by coercion and violence.

The strike was broken by the staff with violence. Housing units were teargassed and many inmates were forced to run a gauntlet of prison staff members who were armed with ax handles (Office of the Attorney General, 1980b; Colvin, 1992). Leaders of the strike were identified and segregated or transferred out of state. The stable inmate leadership, which had been the impetus for inmate social cohesion, was thus systematically eliminated. The prison staff, after this point, began to rely increasingly on coercion to maintain control of the institution. The "hole," which had been closed since 1968, was reopened and used frequently; the number of inmates in disciplinary segregation grew substantially (from less than 5 percent of the inmate population before June 1976 to as much as 25 percent of the inmate population after June 1976).

As this crackdown on organized inmate activity continued at the prison, the corrections department was undergoing rapid and confusing organizational changes. Turnover in the state's top corrections post occurred repeatedly, with five different heads of the corrections department between 1975 and 1980. A similar turnover in the warden's position took place, with five penitentiary wardens between 1975 and 1980. This administrative confusion resulted in inconsistent policy directives from the top of the organization and in the emergency of a middle-level clique of administrators who were virtually unaccountable to anyone in authority. This clique of administrators, by the middle of 1978, had been left to run the prison in any fashion they saw fit.

Under this middle-level clique, there were growing inconsistencies in both security procedures and discipline of inmates. Some shift supervisors followed very closely the proper security procedures; others did not follow them at all. Lax security had long been a problem at PNM, but the tendency toward inconsistency in security operations worsened after 1978 when various shift supervisors ran the prison at their own discretion. Similar problems of inconsistency in discipline were also evident. Some shift captains would enforce rules, at times inappropriately placing inmates in the "hole" for minor violations, while other shift captains would fail to punish some major violations of rules. Consistency in operation and a set routine provides stability for an institution. At PNM, it was difficult for inmates to calculate which behaviors would be punished or when they would be punished. Inmates were thus kept off balance.

This inconsistency by the prison staff was often interpreted by inmates as blatant harassment. In some cases, correctional officers, including some lieutenants and captains, were caught up in a game of mutual harassment with inmates. The game proceeded through interactions in which an officer would verbally humiliate an inmate and the inmate would respond in kind. Often this led to confrontations in which the inmate was led off to disciplinary segregation. The minority of prison officers who engaged in these activities poisoned relations between the staff and inmates and created enormous hostility.

As the middle-level administrators gained dominance after 1978, a new coercive "snitch system" emerged. This system had its roots in the aftermath of the June 1976 inmate strike when staff members attempted to identify the strike leaders. Inmates were threatened with disciplinary lockup if they did not identify strike participants and leaders. By 1978, these tactics had become a key aspect of the institution's inmate control system. Since inmates were not forthcoming with voluntary information, many members of the correctional staff began soliciting information through threats and promises. Inmates were promised early parole consideration, protection, and transfer to minimum-security institutions. They were also threatened with being locked up in disciplinary segregation or, in other cases, were refused protective custody if they did not inform. Another coercive tactic was to intimidate an inmate by threatening to "hang a snitch jacket" on him. This tactic, which involved the threat of labeling an inmate a "snitch" (or informant) was used to solicit information, gain control over an inmate, and, in some instances, retaliate against an inmate.

This came to be known as the "snitch game." The "snitch game" had the effect of breaking apart any sense of inmate solidarity. As the official report (Office of the Attorney General, 1980b:24-25) on the riot maintained:

> The "snitch game" . . . create[d] suspicion and antagonism among
> inmates. "You can't event trust your old friends," was a sentiment
> voiced by several inmates. Inmate opinions of "snitches" included
> this often-repeated characterization, "It's just like in a war. You're
> all on the same side. It's us (inmates) against them (guards). And
> it's the same mentality. If you cross to the other side, you're no more,
> no less than a traitor and a spy." In the late '70s correctional staff's
> increased use of the "snitch game" for information promoted enmi-
> ty among inmates. In fact, some prison staff attempted to use the

hatred which the snitch game created in the inmate society as a means of controlling inmates. In order to coerce particular information from an inmate, some staff members threatened to tell other inmates that he was a snitch. The inmate would usually capitulate, knowing the consequences of wearing a "snitch jacket." The consequences could be severe. First, snitches became more easily identifiable because a few guards were reckless or careless about protecting the identify of inmates who provided information. . . . Inmates also knew that the prison increasingly used Cellblock 4 as a place to house and to protect "snitches" after they were "used up." Second, inmates and staff attributed some of the increase in violence during the late '70s to the motivation for revenge against "snitches." This vengeful violence reached its horrible climax in the 1980 riot.

Some inmates labeled as "snitches" may not have been informants at all. Correctional officers discussed with attorney general investigators the labeling of inmates as "snitches" as a coercive tactic (quoted in Colvin, 1992:154).

> *Correctional Officer:* If I was a guard and he was an inmate and I didn't like him, I'd punch it around and say, "Hey, man, let's put a snitch jacket on this guy." And another inmate come up behind me and I'd say "Hey man, this dude dropped a dime on this guy over here." They'll put a "jacket" on you and life expectancy with a "jacket" on you isn't too long. And that's what [gives names of several PNM administrators, captains, and lieutenants] all of them would do. If they didn't like you, they'd put a jacket on you, plain and simple. . . . I caught [name of correctional officer] lying about another inmate to four or five inmates and the other inmates turned around and looked at him and said, "We'll take care of this."
>
> *Interviewer:* What was the purpose of doing this?
>
> *Correctional Officer:* To get even . . . If I was to walk up to an inmate and just started kicking the hell out of him, I would have a lawsuit on me, but what goes on behind closed doors, only the inmates know.

Whether an inmate had actually been an informant or not, the label of "snitch" could have deadly consequences, a fact that was used to intimidate inmates and create friction among prisoners. After inmate solidarity displayed during the June 1976 strike moved the prison administration to smash inmate organization and leadership, the inmate society became more fragmented and violent. From 1969 through July 1976 there were no killings at PNM, no prison officers were attacked, and inmate fights and sexual assaults were rare. From August 1976 to January 1980, six inmates were killed by other inmates, several attacks on prison officers occurred, and fighting among inmates became routine. And sexual assaults, by the late 1970s, had become so routine that there was "at least one reported case a day [and] 10 to 15 more non-reported cases daily" (*Albuquerque Journal,* 9/16/79:B1).

The administration's tactics for breaking up inmate solidarity led to a series of changes within the inmate society that spawned violence and disorder. As inmate groups broke down into small, self-protective cliques, forces within the inmate society that formerly were capable of holding back disorder and violence among inmates diminished. The lack of inmate leaders in the late 1970s meant that new inmates entering PNM were no longer under the restraints of an established order among inmates. Inmates could no longer socialize new arrivals to the increasingly unstable environment. Some of the new inmates directly challenged the power and control exercised by older inmates who had not already been removed by the administration.

While many observers relate the growing inmate violence to newly arriving inmates, it does not appear that the violent behavior was being imported from outside. Rather, new inmates, as never before, were entering a disorganized social situation with undefined roles and lack of leadership. As they confronted, and were confronted by, this increasingly chaotic situation, many of the new inmates resorted to violence. That the violence was not imported from outside is supported by data on inmates' convictions. In 1970, 45 percent of all crimes for which New Mexico prisoners were convicted were violent crimes. By 1975, the figure had dropped to 38 percent, and by 1979 it was 33 percent (Department of Corrections, 1971, 1976, 1980). Also, a profile of PNM inmates compiled in 1977 (when the inmate violence began increasing dramatically) by consultants for the New Mexico Corrections Master Plan indicated that in comparison to national averages, PNM inmates were relatively nonviolent and unsophisticated in the criminal activity that led to their convictions (Governor's Council on Criminal Justice Planning, 1978).

Rather than importing the violence, inmates were becoming more violent in reaction to a prison social structure that elicited such a response. With a paucity of inmate leaders to guide and ease the transition to prison life for younger inmates, these new inmates were left to their own devices to deal with the fear of assault. By 1978, the fear of being assaulted, especially of being sexually attacked, had become a prevalent feature of inmate life, especially for younger inmates. These new inmates were faced with a deadly dilemma that increasingly set the tone of inmate relations in the late 1970s. The fear created by violent confrontations, or by the mere anticipation of them, produced inmates who either submitted to the exploitation of other inmates (became "punks"), sought protection from officials (became "snitches"), or fought (to prove themselves as "good people" to other inmates by developing a reputation as violent). Most inmates agreed that the only rational choice when faced with the irrational confrontation of a sexual assault was to fight viciously and develop a reputation as someone who others "did not mess with." The other choices, submission or official protection, would lead to a prison experience of perpetual victimization.

In the late 1970s, confrontational situations among inmates sharply increased, forcing more inmates into the deadly dilemma of choosing a course of action against assaults. Some submitted and were marked as punks or homosexuals. This submission did not label them necessarily as sexual deviants but, more importantly, as "morally weak" individuals who would not stand up for themselves. Inmates who chose to seek protective custody, who in the inmates' vocabulary "pc'd up," were also seen as "weak" inmates who could not withstand the pressures of prison life. Added to being marked as weak was the stigma of being a snitch, since it was widely believed among inmates (though by no means always true) that protective custody was a payoff for informing. For "regular" inmates who were "on line" standing up for themselves in the daily battles with other inmates and the prison staff, an inmate who gives in to pressure from other inmates by not standing up for himself, and then gives in to pressure from the administration by informing, was truly a person of "weak moral character." A snitch label (whether deserved or not) thus implies the weakest of inmates who were so low as to sell out their fellow inmates because of fear and intimidation. These inmates were allowing both other inmates *and* the administration to humiliate them. Succumbing to other people's attempts at humiliation is the worst possible fate for a convict (Abbott, 1981). Fear of humiliation drove much of the violence in the inmate society. Violent confrontations were events in which inmates' characters ("weak" or "strong") were being tested. They were also situations in which reputations for violence were being built.

Developing a reputation for violence became a full-time activity as a growing number of inmates were confronted by the prison's deadly dilemma. As inmates vied for violent reputations, the number of confrontational incidents between inmates increased. This competition for violent reputations accelerated the cycle of confrontations and produced a growing number of both violence-prone inmates and those who were perceived as weak. Under these circumstances, the struggle involved in relegating inmates to the roles of victims or victimizers became a monotonous, horrifying, daily occurrence.

The violence led to further fragmentation of the inmate society. Inmates increasingly formed into small cliques for self-protection. These cliques did not constitute the types of gang structures witnessed in other prisons (Irwin, 1980; Jacobs, 1977). For the most part, these cliques were very loosely organized groupings that provided inmates small, often temporary, "ecological niches" (Hagel-Seymour, 1988) relatively free from the violence of the prison.

Some inmate groups began to emerge as influential in 1978. The ACLU lawsuit against PNM (*Duran v. Apodaca*) gave a few Chicano inmates a limited leadership role within some inmate factions. These inmates were directly involved in negotiations for settlement of the lawsuit. But this leadership role was diminishing by late 1979 as the negotiations in the lawsuit bogged down because of disagreements among state officials over issues involved in the lawsuit. Inmates, generally, began to perceive little gain from the lawsuit and the inmates involved in it began to lose influence.

Other inmate cliques gained power by 1978 because of their violent reputations. In 1976 and 1977, Anglo convicts were very disorganized and were regularly attacked by Chicano inmates. Then, some strong Anglo cliques began to surface in 1977. One of the more notorious cliques was associated with three Anglo inmates who, on April 16, 1978, beat another Anglo inmate to death with a baseball bat for allegedly being a snitch. This clique emerged as an important power that struggled with other inmate cliques for dominance.

The inmates caught up in the competition for dominance and violent reputations composed PNM's hardcore cliques. While the total number of inmates involved in these hardcore cliques was about 150 of the more than 1,000 inmates in the prison, their behavior and disruptiveness set the tone for inmate social relations. In stark contrast to the early 1970s, when inmate leaders helped keep the lid on violence among inmates, inmate leadership, to the extent that it existed at all, fell by 1979 to these small, hardcore cliques of inmates who actively engaged in violence and disruption. These hardcore cliques, produced inadvertently by the administration's coercive tactics used to break up inmate solidarity, were leading the inmate society toward an implosion of violence. Inmate solidarity had indeed been eliminated by 1980. But the administration's control of the prison was now more precarious than ever. Their coercive tactics, including use of the "snitch game," produced a fragmented inmate society that promoted inmate-on-inmate violence. The riot that exploded at 1:40 a.m. on February 2, 1980, would reflect this fragmented inmate society and the coercive tactics of control that produced an inmate society.

Overview of the 1980 Riot at the Penitentiary of New Mexico

There were a number of forewarnings that a major disturbance was imminent, yet no decisive actions were taken. Forewarnings included a mix of rumors and intelligence, none of which could be confirmed. Officials had no way to distinguish reliable from unreliable information, a legacy of the coercive snitch system which often resulted in inmates telling officials anything (whether true or not) to escape punishment or receive protection. As it turned out, among the many rumors was one specific bit of information, concerning a possible hostage-taking, that was an accurate forewarning.

Shortly after midnight, on February 2, 1980, the evening and morning shifts completed a count of inmates in the institution, which held 1,157 inmates that night, including 34 in a modular unit outside the main penitentiary building. All inmates were accounted for at the time of the count. About 1 a.m., two groups composed of four correctional officers each began a routine check of all cellhouses and dormitories in the south wing of the prison. [See diagram of the prison, inside front cover.] At 1:40 a.m., one group, which included the shift captain, entered Dorm E-2, the upstairs dormitory in the E-wing.

Inmates in Dorm E-2 had been drinking "home brew" made of yeast and raisins smuggled in from the prison's kitchen. The inmates, sometime between 12:30 a.m. and 1:15 a.m., had hastily agreed upon a plan to jump the guards during their routine check of the dorm. It was not clear whether the plan included an attempt to exit the dormitory. Hostages would be taken in the dormitory; and if the entry door could be successfully jumped, additional hostages would be taken in the south wing of the prison. Beyond the plan to take some guards hostage, the inmates had no idea of what they would do next.

At 1:40 a.m., the dormitory door and the three officers who had just entered Dorm E-2 were jumped simultaneously. Inmates quickly overpowered the officer at the door and the other officers inside the dormitory. The guard at the door had the keys to other dormitories. Four hostages were then under the control of these inmates, who now had access to the main corridor.

At 1:45 a.m., inmates from Dorm E-2 jumped the officer outside Dorm F-2, seized the keys he held to other dormitories, and captured two other guards who were just entering Dorm F-2. A third guard, who had just entered the dorm, ran into the dayroom at the opposite end of the dorm; he was protected by some sympathetic Dorm F-2 inmates, who later helped him escape the prison. Total hostages were now eight, including the protected guard in the Dorm F-2 dayroom.

By 1:50 a.m., hundreds of inmates were milling around the main corridor in the south wing of the prison. At 1:57 a.m., two guards leaving the officers' mess hall, located in the central area of the institution, saw inmates beating and dragging a naked man (later identified as a hostage guard) up the south corridor toward the grill that separated the south wing from the central area of the prison. They also noticed that this corridor grill, contrary to prison policy, was open. Inmates were about to come through the opened grill. The two guards then raced north up the main corridor, passing the control center and entering the north wing of the prison, closing the corridor grill to the north wing behind them. Soon, scores of inmates were in front of the control center, which was separated from the rioters by what was supposed to be "shatterproof" glass. Inmates used a metal-canister fire extinguisher, pulled from the wall in the main corridor, to break the control center glass. The control center officers ran toward the front entrance of the prison and to the safety of the Tower 1 gatehouse. The inmates entered the control center through the smashed window and trashed its interior, sending keys flying in all directions from the key PegBoards.

By 2:02 a.m., inmates had gained access to the north wing and to the administration wing, since the grills to these areas were opened electronically from the control center. It took the inmates time to find keys to specific cellblocks since keys were scattered by those inmates who first breached the control center, which indicates the unplanned nature of the takeover. But by 3 a.m., inmates had found the key to the disciplinary unit, Cellblock 3. Here they captured three more correctional officers, bringing the total to 11 hostages. (By this point, two guards had hidden themselves in the crawl space in the basement of Cellblock 5, where they remained undetected by rioters throughout the riot. And the hospital technician locked himself and seven inmate-patients into the upstairs floor of the Hospital Unit, where they also remained undetected until the riot was over.) *Those unnoticed*

The first inmate killings during the riot occurred in Cellblock 3 at about 3:15 a.m. An inmate, shouting in Spanish, "No era yo. No lo hice." ("It wasn't me. I didn't do it.") was beaten, tortured, and mutilated. This inmate was assumed to have informed on other inmates who were also locked in the disciplinary unit. Another inmate, who was mentally disturbed and apparently had kept other Cellblock 3 inmates awake at night with his screams, was shot in the head at close range with a canister fired from a tear-gas launcher taken from the control center.

At about the same time, another group of inmates had found keys to the prison pharmacy, located on the first floor of the Hospital Unit. The pharmacy contained narcotics, barbiturates, and sedatives, which were ingested in massive doses by inmates throughout the riot.

Other inmates in the early morning hours of the first day of the riot found keys to the basement area of the prison, below the kitchen. Here they retrieved an acetylene blowtorch that was used at about 3:15 a.m. to open the far south corridor grill, leading to the Educational Unit and Dorm D-1, which contained the twelfth (and last) guard to be taken hostage. This blowtorch was later taken to the other end of the prison to open the far north corridor grill and Cellblock 5. Cellblock 5 was vacant due to renovation. But construction crews had left in the Cellhouse 2 additional acetylene torches. Later, these blowtorches would be used to open Cellblock 4, the Protective Custody unit.

The period between 3 a.m. and 7 a.m. was characterized by chaos, infighting, and violence. There was no leadership throughout the riot. Inmates' actions were completely uncoordinated. Some inmates were setting fires in the administrative offices, others in the Psychological Unit. At certain points, inmates manning walkie-talkies radioed for firefighting crews to come into the prison; when firefighters approached the prison they were driven back by other inmates who threw debris at them. Other inmates were fighting, forming into groups for self-protection, or hiding in fear.

While all these uncoordinated activities and fighting were going on during the early hours of the riot, a few inmates who had been released from Cellblock 3 and Cellhouse 6 discussed organizing the riot into a protest against the administration. These inmates included those involved in the ACLU lawsuit (*Duran v. Apodaca*). They managed in the early hours of the riot to get control of the three hostages captured in Cellblock 3. However, they were able to gain control of only one of the other nine hostages. The other hostages were being held by various groups in the south wing of the institution. A few were held by sympathetic inmates who protected them. The shift captain was moved frequently and may have been under the control of different groups throughout the riot, some of whom beat him mercilessly, others of whom tended to his wounds and protected him. Unlike the three hostages who were captured in Cellblock 3, who were treated relatively well for the remainder of the riot, many of the hostages held in the south wing of the prison were beaten, stabbed, and sodomized.

The Cellblock 3 and Cellhouse 6 inmates who were attempting to organize the riot into a protest had little influence on the behavior of the rioting inmates. One inmate, who identified himself as a leader in this attempt to turn the riot into a protest, said:

> There were a few of us in here that were trying to freeze that [inmate-to-inmate violence] because it was wrong, it was dead wrong. Three hours after the riot started there was no stopping it. But there were a few of us that were saying, "Hey, if you want to burn it down, burn it down or tear it up or whatever you want, but quit killing people and don't turn this thing against ourselves. If you got to fight somebody now, fight the Man, fight the administration" (quoted in Colvin, 1992:183-184).

But his and the other inmates' efforts to turn the riot into a protest were futile.

As fights began to break out in the south wing of the prison, injuries to inmates and killings began to increase. Many of the deaths that occurred in the south wing were the result of fights between small groups of inmates and between individuals. Fights over hostages held in the south wing occurred. Many inmates, perceived as weak or defenseless, were attacked and raped; those offering resistance were beaten severely, a few were killed. Some assaults in the south wing appeared to be random. Inmates suffered injuries when they were hacked with meat cleavers, stabbed, or hit with pipes for no reasons apparent to the victims. A few of the killings in the south wing also appear to have been random. Of the 33 killings during the riot, 17 occurred in the south wing, many in the early morning hours of the first day. Of the approximately 400 injuries and rapes, the vast majority also occurred in the south wing.

More inmates would have been killed had Dorm E-1 been entered by the rioters. This semi-protection unit's inmates successfully fought off attempts by rioters to enter this dorm. A sympathetic inmate, who had some friends in the unit, tossed a three-foot long wrench through a hole in the wire mesh above the dorm entrance. This inmate was immediately jumped by other inmates in the main corridor who had observed this action; he was beaten to death. But because he had tossed them this heavy wrench the Dorm E-1 inmates were able to knock bars out of a window at the rear of the dormitory and make it to the perimeter fence and surrender to authorities for safety. Up to 80 inmates housed in the semi-protection unit were saved by this inmate's action.

The most horrific killings of the riot occurred in the north wing of the penitentiary, specifically in Cellblock 4, the Protective Custody unit. By 7 a.m., small groups of inmates entered Cellblock 4 after burning through its entrance grills with blowtorches. As these inmates entered the cellblock, they began shouting the names of intended victims. As rioting inmates operated the control panels that gang locked and unlocked cell doors, many Cellblock 4 inmates were able to leave their cells, blend in with the rioters, and escape the carnage. Other Cellblock 4 inmates were not so fortunate. On tiers where inmates had jammed the locks to their cell grills, the gang locking and unlocking mechanisms would not operate. These inmates were trapped in their cells. Using blowtorches, rioting inmates cut through the bars of entrance grills to the individual cells containing inmates. As the intended victims suffered through the agonizing wait while their cells were entered, they were taunted and told in vivid detail exactly how they would be tortured and killed.

These protective custody inmates were apparently killed by four or five small groups, containing three to five inmates each. The groups appeared to have acted independently in choosing victims. Inmates were tortured, stabbed, mutilated, burned, bludgeoned, hanged, and thrown off upper-tier catwalks into the basement. One Cellblock 4 inmate, a 36-year-old African-American, was killed and decapitated. Whether this occurred in the cellblock or elsewhere in the prison could not be established by investigators. His head was reportedly placed on a pole, paraded through the main corridor, and shown to the guards captured in Cellblock 3. This inmate's body was later deposited outside the prison's front entrance with the head stuffed between the legs. Another inmate, while reportedly still alive, had a steel rod hammered completely through his head. One inmate victim was drenched with glue and set on fire. Other atrocities were also reported to investigators.

There was an apparent competition between the groups in both the quantity and "quality" of their killings. There does not appear to have been any motive, such as personal revenge, to account for these killings. No particular inmate killer among the suspects, for example, had apparently been "snitched off" by any of the victims. In fact, only a few of the inmates killed in Cellblock 4 were later identified by staff and inmates as suspected informants. These inmate victims were viewed as "weak" inmates and thus vulnerable targets of violence, whose deaths would not be avenged by other inmates. The fact that the victims were trapped in protective isolation not only increased the killers' sense of total domination but demonstrated the killers' "superiority" since they outsmarted the state authorities who were charged with protecting these inmate victims. In addition, a group dynamic of proving one's commitment to deviance was amplified in Cellblock 4 since small groups of inmates were competing for images as dominatingly "awesome" deviants. (See Jack Katz [1981] for a discussion of the dynamics involved in cold-blooded killings.) Each group felt compelled to outdo the other in its acts of violence. These brutal acts marked their victims as "morally weak" and their perpetrators as "morally superior" in the upside-down world that the inmate society had become. Inmates involved in these killings could count on gaining reputations as the most violent and feared inmates in the prison.

Most of the Cellblock 4 killings were apparently over by 10 a.m. on the first morning of the riot. More inmates would have undoubtedly died had they not been able to escape Cellblock 4. Besides those inmates who left their cells and escaped the protective custody unit when it was opened, other inmates living in this unit were rescued by sympathetic inmates. Some individual inmates entered Cellblock 4, found specific inmate friends, and sneaked them out of the unit. One contingent of about 20 African-American inmates from Cellhouse 6 converged on Cellblock 4 about 7:30 a.m. to rescue one of their leaders, a Black Muslim minister, who had been locked in the protection unit. Upon his release, the Muslim minister told his followers to get as many protective custody inmates out of Cellblock 4 as possible. This group saved many of the intended victims (Anglo, Hispanic, and African-American) from certain death. They brought these inmates to Cellhouse 6 where they combined forces for self-protection. At about noon, on the first day of the riot, they were able to fight their way to Dorm E-1 and leave the prison through the rear window that had been broken open earlier.

By noon on the first day, many inmates had managed to find routes from which to exit the prison and surrender to authorities who controlled the perimeter fence. By 5 p.m., more than 350 inmates had left the prison. They would continue to stream out of the prison for the rest of the riot. By 1 p.m. on the second (and final) day of the riot, only 100 of the prison's 1,157 inmates remained inside.

The final morning of the riot saw the setting of more fires, an increasingly larger stream of inmates leaving the prison to surrender to authorities, inmates being rushed to hospitals for injuries and pharmacy-drug overdoses, and bodies of inmates being deposited in the yard in front of the prison. Intermittent negotiations between state authorities and some prisoners continued and seemed to reach a climax by the final morning of the riot.

Throughout the riot, sporadic attempts at negotiating the release of hostages were made by state authorities. Negotiations were complicated by the fact that more than one group controlled hostages, and some of these groups had no interest in negotiating release. Three hostages were released at different times either in anticipation of or in response to talking to the news media. At one point, an NBC cameraman entered the prison's entrance lobby and recorded inmate's grievances. The lobby was filled with smoke as inmates presented their grievances about poor food, nepotism, harassment, overcrowding, idleness, inadequate recreation facilities, and arbitrary discipline practices by the administration. At another point, two inmates met with two news reporters just outside the entrance of the prison building. Beyond the release of these three hostages, however, negotiations with inmates had very little to do with the release of hostages or ending the riot.

Two hostages managed, with the help of sympathetic inmates, to leave the prison disguised as inmates. Other hostages were released by inmates because these inmates feared these hostages might die from injuries, which they thought would provoke an immediate retaking of the prison. One other hostage was released after an apparent agreement emerged from negotiations.

At about 8:30 a.m. on February 3, the second (and last) day of the riot, three Hispanic inmates (Lonnie Duran, Vincent Candelaria, and Kendrick Duran), who were among the few inmates attempting, unsuccessfully, to organize the riot into a protest over prison conditions, ironed out an agreement for ending the riot with prison authorities during a meeting in the gatehouse beneath Tower 1. The agreement had five points: (1) no retaliation against rioting inmates; (2) segregation policies be reviewed; (3) inmates be permitted to meet with the press; (4) no double-bunking of inmates in Cellblock 3; and (5) inmates be given water hoses to douse fires inside the prison. The Durans and Candelaria returned to the prison to seek approval from other inmates. They re-emerged from the prison shortly before noon for continued negotiations. By noon, only two hostages remained in the prison.

The final hour of negotiations leading up to the end of the riot was witnessed by reporter Peter Katel who later, with co-author Michael Serrill, gave the following account:

> The two Durans and Candelaria emerged from the prison and announced that they had approval from other inmates to sign the agreement negotiated [earlier that morning]. . . . Then negotiations became more complicated. Other inmates joined the Durans and Candelaria at the negotiating table. They haggled over exactly how the agreement was to be implemented by prison officials. . . . Officials were particularly worried about the presence of three new inmates, William Jack Stephens, Michael Colby and Michael Price, at the negotiations. Colby and Stephens escaped on Dec. 9 and were recaptured. . . . In 1978, they, together with Price, beat another inmate to death with baseball bats. . . . Their commitment to a peaceful resolution of the riot was considered dubious. Later, they were identified as prime suspects in some of the [riot] killings. . . .

> At about 12:30 p.m., Colby, Stephens and other inmates rejoined the talks and started making new demands. . . . [Deputy Corrections Director Felix] Rodriguez says that at this point he began to worry that the Durans and Candelaria were losing control. He also began to wonder whether the majority of inmates inside were really aware of and had agreed to the five rather mild demands (Serrill & Katel, 1980:21).

Rodriguez, fearing that Colby and Stephens were gaining control of the situation, made a deal with them. He promised to transport them immediately to another prison out of state and told them to go back inside the prison to get their belongings. As soon as Colby and Stephens left, Rodriguez ordered Vincent Candelaria and Lonnie and Kendrick Duran (the inmates with whom he had been negotiating) to get the remaining two hostages, who were now seated blindfolded on the grass outside the main entrance. A few minutes later, at about 1:30 p.m., these last hostages were brought to Rodriguez. Immediately, police, National Guardsmen, and prison employees rushed the prison to retake it from the approximately 100 inmates still within. Authorities encountered no resistance from inmates during the retaking of the prison. No shots were fired. The riot was over.

Summary

The 1980 riot was a dramatic and explosive episode in a continuing pattern of disorder that had its roots several years earlier. Two things stand out as characteristics of the 1980 riot at PNM: the almost total lack of organization by inmates and the inmate-to-inmate violence that punctuated the event. The extreme violence was caused by a small number of inmates who belonged to some particularly violent inmate cliques. The emergence of these violent inmate cliques was largely an organizational phenomenon. They had their origin in the 1976 shift in tactics of inmate control, when measures, including the coercive snitch system, were used to undermine inmate solidarity. As inmate solidarity disintegrated, young prisoners began entering a social situation that elicited violence from a growing number of inmates. These social dynamics came together in the early morning hours of February 2, 1980 to produce the most horrific prison riot in history.

With an understanding of this background and an overview of the event itself, the reader now has a context in which to place the following account of the riot by Mike Rolland. Rolland was housed in Cellhouse 2 on the night the riot started. His account is based on his own experience and on conversations he has had with others who survived the event. Rolland has captured the pure horror of the event and gives us an understanding of what it is like to live through such an experience.

References

Abbott, Jack Henry (1981). *In the Belly of the Beast.* New York, NY: Vintage.

Albuquerque Journal (1979). "Prison Sexual Brutality Changes Inmate." Sept. 16, Sec. B, p. 1.

Colvin, Mark (1992). *The Penitentiary in Crisis: From Accommodation to Riot in New Mexico.* Albany, NY: SUNY Press.

Department of Corrections (1980). *Annual Report.* Santa Fe, NM: State of New Mexico.

———— (1976). *Annual Report.* Santa Fe, NM: State of New Mexico.

———— (1971). *Annual Report.* Santa Fe, NM: State of New Mexico.

Governor's Council on Criminal Justice Planning (1978). "Technical Report 6: Inmate Profile." *Sourcebook for New Mexico Corrections Planning.* Santa Fe, NM: State of New Mexico.

Hagel-Seymour, John (1988). "Environmental Sanctuaries for Susceptible Prisoners." In Robert Johnson & Hans Toch (eds.) *The Pains of Imprisonment,* pp. 267-284. Prospect Hills, IL: Waveland Press.

Irwin, John (1980). *Prisons in Turmoil.* Boston, MA: Little, Brown.

Jacobs, James B. (1977). *Stateville: The Penitentiary in Mass Society.* Chicago, IL: University of Chicago Press.

Katz, Jack (1988). *Seductions of Crime.* New York, NY: Basic Books.

Officers of Attorney General (1980a). *Report of the Attorney General on the February 2 and 3, 1980 Riot at the Penitentiary of New Mexico, Part I.* Santa Fe, NM: State of New Mexico.

———— (1980b). *Report of the Attorney General on the February 2 and 3 Riot at the Penitentiary of New Mexico, Part II.* Santa Fe, NM: State of New Mexico.

Serrill, Michael S. & Peter Katel (1980). "New Mexico: The Anatomy of a Riot." *Corrections Magazine,* 6(April):6-24.

Wicker, Tom (1975). *A Time to Die.* New York, NY: Ballantine.

PART II
DESCENT
INTO MADNESS

Prologue to the Takeover

The New Mexico State Prison riot of 1980 was the bloodiest prison uprising in American history. The events that led up to the early morning takeover were classic penological blunders. The prison administration had become a clique of good ole boys answerable to no one. Court orders were ignored by the Attorney General's office. This had a trickle-down effect for the Corrections Director and Wardens of the facility. They, in turn, ignored the pressure building from an overcrowded penitentiary, placing two and one-half times the prisoners into structures than they were designed to accommodate. They contemptuously ignored the open rumors of rebellion and hostage taking. These rumors had been circulating through the prison for months and were actually laughed at by the officials and staff. The prison was also in the midst of being refurbished, renovated, and modernized.

By the time I got to Santa Fe, I had already seen a measure of blood and violence. I had outlasted Vietnam, but not its lasting effects. When a young man is trained to kill, it's an easy jump for that same youngster to say to himself, "I'll just rob a few banks." When I was medevaced from that war in 1970, I came home to a nation where many considered me a baby-killer. I laid in a hospital bed at Valley Forge and heard the chanting screams of protesters outside. When I joined the Army out of high school, I wanted to go to Vietnam to save my country, to protect my mother and sisters from the commie horde. I wanted to be the best soldier there, and the handful of medals I brought home couldn't get me the time of day. For years I had to deny being a Vietnam vet. When you deny the past, you have no future. During that time when the fabric of American patriotism was torn down the middle, I felt abandoned by my country. The disillusionment of right and wrong became as blurred as the lies my country spoon-fed me. When I started robbing banks, I knew it was illegal but I couldn't consider it wrong. I looked at it with the frame of mind that I wasn't hurting anyone—the government owed me. The anger I felt at being an outcast drove me like a five-ton truck in the obvious direction of confinement. My trip up the river in New Mexico began November 22, 1977. This was my second plunge into prison for being out of control and unable to cope in society. The values I had manifested themselves in not seeing the pain I caused. But none of the experiences I had up until then could prepare me for the pain and madness I saw on February 2 and 3, 1980.

Days before that date, the indifferent Administrators had transferred maximum security prisoners en masse from individual cells to a minimum security, open-bay dorm. This was ordered and done for the ongoing remodeling projects.

As with most monolithic institutions of this sort, a prison needs a large staff to operate correctly. The day before the riot, a change in work shifts had routinely occurred for the guard force. Those who worked days had moved to the night shift, and guards that worked nights were moved to the day shift. This was done every six months to a year to prevent familiarity between guards and prisoners. On the night of the takeover, the guards weren't cognizant of the trap they had made for themselves.

It was count time and the Duty Captain took a Lieutenant and a Sergeant into the dorm to perform this nightly procedure. All the inside keys of the prison were found and taken from the Captain, and the drama that would horrify the nation began.

It's 17 years later and society still doesn't have a handle on its justice system. Recently, America topped the million mark for incarcerated souls. Prisons aren't being built fast enough to keep up with the numbers. Billions are being thrown down the same well with no thought-out solutions or end in sight.

I wrote this story so intelligent people can see what madness is, to put a face on the abstract images that the media left on the public mind. Riot is a place where there is no humanity and even less mercy. Dante wrote about the levels of hell. This is a story about the levels of madness and violence that a person has to survive when looking through that door this side of hades. I live with the memories and I'm able to write about them only because I can box them up again and place them in the back, deepest part of my mind. I hope this little journey into the past will enlighten those prison administrators of the future—what awaits when mistakes are repeated.

1   Kaleidoscope of Rage

We had been playing poker since the supper meal. In a few minutes we'd be locked in our cells for the night. I finished shuffling the deck of cards, got Shorty on my right to cut them, and as I dealt them out to the three players around me I said, "Okay fellas, this is the last hand for the night. This is straight five-card low-ball, make your bets and let's get a big pot." Everyone picked their cards up and inspected their hand for the lowest cards they held.

It had been a long night for me, luck hadn't shined my way all evening. I was house man tonight and the only money I had made was a 10 percent cut of each hand dealt. Hopefully I could do better with this last hand.

Bobby sat on my left and opened the betting with 75¢, a standard opening bet of a player happy with some or most of the five cards he held.

We sat at one of the large steel picnic tables in the television room. The TV was on but no one was watching it. Everyone else in the cellblock had gone to their cell and was probably asleep.

Lucky sat next to Bobby, called the bet and tossed three quarter chips into the center of the table. He had been true to his name tonight by winning most of the money at the table. Lucky always wore dark shades to the game—either for mystique reasons or because he thought his eyes betrayed his hand.

We played poker every Friday and Saturday. On those nights we were allowed to move around in the cellblock till 1:30 a.m. Every other night of the week we were locked in at 10:30 p.m., so the weekends were kind of a treat. In prison, anything to break up the boredom is savored.

Shorty bet next, but he raised the bet a dollar. He's a short, older man who smoked foul-smelling cigars. They actually had the odor of burning rope. He talked around the burning stub in his mouth. "That'll cost everyone a buck seventy-five to play," he said. Then he looked around at everyone in a challenge, tapping his cards against his thumb. It was an obvious bluff.

19

With being house man I kept track of the money in the game. House man also supplied cigarettes and coffee for the players. Every weekend we rotated the house among the regulars who played.

I counted out seven quarter chips from my money and dropped them into the growing pile. This being the last hand for the night, I felt I had to play and I had a pretty good hand myself. Shorty just did me a favor by raising the bet. By just calling his bet I didn't want to call attention to my hand and I'm sure he's blustering. In turn, Bobby called the bet and so did Lucky. Now the pot had seven dollars and I scooped up the deck saying, "Put your discards here," lightly slapping an empty spot on the table in front of me. Bobby asked for and got two cards from the deck. I flicked three cards to Lucky and Shorty only wanted one card. Maybe he wasn't bluffing and I slowly slid one card off the top of the deck for my hand. As soon as I laid the unused deck on the table, Shorty announced that the bet would be three dollars. He held his cards close to his chest to exaggerate the secrecy they held. I casually looked at the money he inserted to be sure it was what he'd said and very slowly thumbed my cards apart. One at a time I peeked at the corners and as I reached the last card, I said a silent prayer to all the Gods for help. It was a Jack and I immediately scornfully passed by tossing my hand on the top of the unused deck of cards. Bobby called and dropped three dollar chips on the pile. Lucky counted three dollars from his quarter chips, set that aside and counted two more as a raised bet. I was just an observer now and mentally counted the money in the center of the table. Hopefully, Lucky would raise the bet and make my cut bigger. He looked at his hand again and reached for the three dollars with his left hand, slid the chips into the center and said, "I'm just gonna call." Now there was sixteen dollars in the pot and my cut would be a buck fifty 'cuz we didn't have or use dime chips. Shorty, Bobby, and Lucky eyed each other, waiting for the other to show their cards first. In poker etiquette, Shorty should have showed his hand first since he made the opening three dollar bet. But in prison none of the proper Hoyle rules were followed. I looked at my watch, knowing they would see the move, and all three flipped their cards over at once. I quickly looked at the laid-out hands. Lucky had an 8-7 low hand, Bobby had a 7-6 and I announced Shorty the winner with a 7-4. He wasn't bluffing after all and he was amusing to watch when he won. He couldn't win gracefully. He had to utter something and let everyone in the room know he was a gambler. I counted out my cut and slid the rest to him.

Just as everyone started counting their chips, three guards came in the cellblock gate entrance with a rattling of keys and shouted for everyone to "lock down." One of the guards stood at the gate entrance while the other two went from cell to cell locking doors and counting the cell occupants. They started on the bottom floor and since we were in the second floor (tier) television room and we all lived on the second tier, we had time to settle up with winners and losers in the game. Finished with that, we filtered out of the TV room and strolled to our individual cells.

Shorty stopped at my cell door puffing on the stub he had in his mouth. He retold the splendid strategy in winning the last hand. It wasn't until the guards came up the stairs to the second tier that he said his goodnight and let my door swing shut.

When the guard locked my cell door I had already finished my nightly ritual of taking off my boots and cleaning up for bed. Nights are all the same in prison, boring and mundane, unless you can find something to occupy your waking hours. I was still wide awake so I flipped through a stack of magazines under my bed until I found one I hadn't read completely.

I had been kicked-back reading in bed for about 20 minutes when I noticed the lights blink on in the cellblock through the small window in my cell door. I didn't pay it any particular attention because the guards had a habit of returning to the cell-block after locking everyone in for the night and picking one or two cells to search for contraband. But it did get my attention when someone ran by my cell door. I dropped the magazine and got up to see what was happening. I thought at first that a guard had flipped out. My field of vision looking out the cell door window wasn't much—I could see the cells immediately across from mine and the one below on the bottom floor. Then I heard the lock box open that controls the cell doors on the bottom floor. It was a distinct grating noise and doors were pushed open and convicts streamed out of their cells on the bottom floor. I couldn't fathom what was going on. Nothing like this had ever occurred at this time of night. Then I heard the lock box again and felt my cell door tremble as the locking device released all the cell doors on the second tier.

I tentatively pushed on my door and as I swung it open, I stood there for a moment startled and gingerly stepped out on the tier. Still unsure, I turned to my right and pulled open Stanley's cell door. He immediately sat up in bed and I said, "Man, I don't know what's going on but all the cells are open. There's no guards around and it's about 2:00 in the morning." He swung his legs out of bed and stood up. Then we both heard someone start yelling, "We got the whole joint and we're gonna tear it up!" I glanced around in the direction of the front entrance of the cell-block and saw convicts running by in the hallway. By then Stanley had moved over and we both stood on the tier in front of our cells in our underwear and bare feet. It dawned on me then and I said out loud, "This is the riot, the takeover that everyone's been talking about." We stood there and watched as the riot got in full swing. Convicts below us on the bottom tier were wrapping towels around their head to cover up their identity. Groups were leaving and coming in the cellblock. One group of convicts brought in cases of cigarettes and candy bars and was giving them out. I had a couple cartons of smokes tossed up to me. Stanley got a handful of candy bars thrown to him. Someone said all the guards on the night shift were taken hostage. We stood at the railing around the tier munching on candy as a group of unidentifi-able convicts ran in and attacked some blacks on the bottom floor. The yelling and screaming got louder and I turned to Stanley and said, "I'm gonna get dressed and check on a friend, do you want to come along?" He excitedly rubbed his hands together and said, "Yea, let's see how much of this prison has been taken." We both immediately went back into our cells and started throwing on clothes and shoes as fast as we could. I put on everything I had on earlier plus my sweatshirt and a blue prison shirt over that. I got my knit cap from the metal dresser cabinet; it wouldn't hide my identity but it would keep my head warm. I didn't believe I'd need to hide my face but I grabbed a towel on my way out of the door anyway.

Stanley had already dressed and was waiting on the tier when I came out. He was my partner, one of the few people I trusted. He led the way down the tier to the stairs and out in the long hallway that runs the full length of the prison. Convicts ran by laughing and shouting. Two guards paraded by with 55-gallon garbage can drums over their heads and upper body. They were prodded along by two convicts with sticks who beat a constant barrage on one side of the drum and then on the other side to keep the guards going in the desired direction. The excitement and noise seemed to have reached a crescendo and hung there, all up and down the hallway. It was a kaleidoscope of madness. We had to shout at each other just to be heard over the noise. Stanley continued to lead the way, threading in and around individuals and groups of convicts in a party-type atmosphere.

It was my intention to get to Dorm B-1 and find Weasel, a long-time friend of mine. We passed a group beating and stabbing a suspected rat (informer). They had him hemmed in against the hallway wall. He attempted to fight, but he was overwhelmed by the sheer number around him. We passed a couple of other cons knocking out the overhead lights with long broom handles. They went in the opposite direction from us, going from light to light. Just as we reached B-1 and E-1, dorms across from each other, we heard yelling coming from the entrance of Dorm E-1. It was a semi-protective custody unit and standing at the door of the unit were five or six convicts brandishing clubs and knives and telling those behind the door to open up and let them in. Those on the inside had stacked their beds against the door, an effective barricade to keep out the rioters. We watched for a couple of minutes as different members of the group outside tried to convince those inside to come out. But those on the inside weren't going for the soft, soothing words or the threats, and it looked like a standoff to me.

We sidled over toward Dorm B-1 entrance while watching the exchange at the Dorm E-1 entrance. Then the noise going on in Dorm B-1 took our full attention. There were crowds of convicts in large and small groups around captured guards being tortured and tormented in various imaginative ways. We pushed through one group and saw a guard tied naked to a bed frame. A fire had been lit under him. He was screaming and struggling, trying to avoid the flames. I just shook my head and backed away. Most of the lights had already been broken out and we literally had to search for Weasel. We walked up on two cons feeding this one guard wads of crackers at once. He was tied to a center post that supported the ceiling. One of the cons punched and slapped the guard, telling him to open his mouth and when he did open it, it was stuffed with crackers and he was told to chew. Then the other con threw hot scalding coffee in his face. The cons both howled in laughter as the hostage guard spit and spewed crackers while trying to scream. I knew this guard. He was called "Big Foot." He was notorious for searching someone coming out of the chow hall after a meal. If he found food on the convict, he gave the convict the choice of either eating the food on the spot or going to lock up. I'd seen convicts get sick from overeating something that "Big Foot" had found on them in order to avoid going to the disciplinary lock up block. Right then "Big Foot" was experiencing a similar humiliation. I finally spotted Weasel in the throng of onlookers. I made my way over to him and asked, "Is this shit crazy enough for you?" He looked surprised to see me and I said, "Come on man, let's get out of here," and we three started for the front of the dorm and entrance. The madness going on was unbelievable. Edging past people and seeing the glee in their eyes as they watched the pain and terror in the eyes of their naked, trembling hostages. Near the door we passed two cons arguing over who would get the privilege of inflicting the next round of pain to the bleeding, tied-up guard at their feet.

Getting out of there was only a brief relief. We walked right into a wall of black smoke rolling out of the Dorm E-1 entrance. A couple of the convicts who had been trying to get into the Dorm E-1 were standing in the hallway in front of the entrance. They both held half-empty gallon bottles of dry-cleaning fluid. There were four other empty bottles laying on the floor. They had filled a mop bucket with the flammable liquid and thrown it through the door and over barricades onto the protective custody cons holding the door closed. The men in there were mostly young and naive and probably just afraid to live in the general population. The regular protective custody unit, Cellblock 4, was overcrowded to the point that the officials had started moving the overflow into Dorm E-1. The officials thought it was safe to keep them all together in this dorm.

We ducked out of the smoke but not before getting a lung full. We coughed our way down the hall, spitting the rank taste from our mouths, trying to get some distance from the area. The crowd of convicts in the hallway surged past us to see what was happening in the fire and smoke.

Stanley said we should look for Boots, a friend of his, in Dorm F-1. That was the young convicts' dorm. We moved on down the hall in the opposite direction we'd come through just minutes ago. The rat we'd seen getting stabbed earlier was now being dragged by two convicts, pulled by a sheet that had been tied around his neck. They'd drag him a little ways and someone would pounce on his body for a gruesome ride. One after another they'd act like they were riding a bronco, stabbing the body as fast and as many times as they could. Then slide off to the side laughing as another leaped on. One convict just sat down on the legs and stabbed him three or four times, pulling the blade through the body in long renting gashes. And on down the hallway this bloody smear went in front of us.

No one said anything, just stared at the grisly scene and then we turned in at the Dorm F-1 entrance. There weren't very many convicts in the dorm and no one I recognized. The lights in the TV room were on at the far end of the dorm. We shuffled on between the bunk beds toward the lights thinking that Boots might be watching TV. In passing the windows between the dorm and TV room I noticed that mattresses lined the floor inside, like mats on a high school gym floor. It was puzzling at first glance, but when I pulled the door open it became crystal clear. I opened the door and took two steps inside and stopped. On most of the mattresses were tied naked, young-looking men staring up at me. They were all gagged. An older convict who was bent over one of the youngsters looked up and shouted, "Hey, what the *hell* do you want?" At the same instant three other half-dressed convicts bolted off the table with knives drawn. I immediately said, "Excuse me!" Holding my hands up to show my mistake for walking in on them, and stepped on Stanley backing out. And all in one motion, I shut the TV room door. We may have looked foolish and weak from stepping on each other trying to make haste in vacating the immediate encampment. But in prison there's two things most important not to interfere with—a convict's money and sexual gratification, and I'm not thrilled about fighting anyone with a knife when I have nothing. So, looking foolish in getting away from three knife-wielding homos didn't bother me in the least. No one I knew or cared about was in the room, so it was none of my business. I didn't believe Boots would be among those on the mattress anyway, so we trooped back into the screaming insanity of the hallway. We didn't know where else to look for Boots and automatically we turned left toward our living area. I'd had enough exploring for the moment and as we trudged into the entrance of Cellhouse 2, Boots and another friend, John, came out of Cellhouse 1, just across the hall from us.

They said they had been looking for us and we stood in the hallway and talked about the merriment swell around us. Further down the hallway, towards the heart of the prison, the racket was even louder.

None of us had ever experienced a riot or seen such boiling insanity before. People continued to stream by, screaming and whooping about the new scope of their unrestrained liberty. We just naturally followed the frenzy toward its center.

2   Theft on Our Minds

We followed the stream of rioters toward the dining hall, gym, Captain's office, and canteen. The destruction was centered on inanimate state property. At the double doors to the convict dining room we watched as rioters tore apart the appliances that were used at meal time. An ice machine had been ripped from the attached plumbing and water fountained upward from the broken pipes. The milk dispenser was already laying on its side and two convicts were slinging flat pieces of metal from it across the room like frisbees. Two new water coolers that had been installed recently were wrenched from the connecting pipes and water squirted in two different directions. It was already starting to run out into the hallway at our feet. We moved on to the gym across from the dining hall. Rioters were ripping the curtains from the windows and stage area where movies were shown. One convict had a weight from the weightlifting room and was walking up and down the wooden bleachers. He dropped it on the seats one after another, shattering them into splinters. Just a few feet from the gym doors the Captain's office burst into flames, and everyone in the area scurried back laughing and pointing at this symbol of authority that was cooking with contempt. The fire burned so hot that we had to stay close to the far wall to get passed. At the canteen, it had already been thoroughly looted, but the rioters were still tearing the store apart. One convict had a weightlifting bar and he'd lift it over his head and crash it down on the empty shelves, splintering three and four shelves in one swing. It wasn't enough to clean out the canteen of all food items and radios. These guys were determined to completely destroy the room. Then as we got closer to the control center, the heart of prison security, the destruction was breathtaking. One of the remodeling projects recently completed here on the control center was to take out the security bars and small, square, unattractive windows and replace them with mirrored, unbreakable sheets of glass. All this unbreakable glass was shattered and the main control center was wide open. Of course, we went in to see what was so special about this room. All the control panels were smashed and hanging from threads of wire like confetti scattered around a room after a party. The

25

only reason that it wasn't on fire was because there wasn't anything to burn. All the grill bar gates around the control center were standing open. The hallway to the front of the prison was open. The administrative section, secretary offices, Deputy Warden's office, and visiting room were open. This entire area beyond the control center was an area where convicts were not generally allowed without a guard escort. We passed offices that were being ransacked by rioters. Some were reading files that were found, others were stacking files and papers on desktops and lighting them on fire. Convicts rushed by us with gallon bottles of dry-cleaning fluid. We passed a group standing by central files, a huge, round, drum-like file that revolved at the touch of a button. They were turning the files and pouring the flammable liquid back and forth across the file fronts. We heard it explode in a loud "crump" behind us. At the next grill bar gate we split up. One gate led to the right and to the lobby and front of the prison. John, Boots, and Weasel said they wanted to see what the front of the prison looked like. The other grill bar gate led to the left and upstairs to the Parole Board offices and prison investigator's office. That is the gate that Stanley and I went through. There was a group of convicts already in the Parole Board office stacking files on the table and lighting fires. We went down a short hallway to the investigator's office. It was unlocked and Stanley and I started rifling through everything.

Stanley got into the desk drawers and I went in a large closet with four connecting doors that slid back. There was a rack of guard uniforms on hangers, boxes of papers in the bottom. On the shelf above the uniforms I found paper bags with names and dates written on the outside. Inside the paper bags were plastic baggies with marijuana inside them. I immediately liberated all these bags and stuffed them into my shirt. I told Stanley what I had found and he showed me a gold watch with diamonds on the face that he had taken from the desk. We both laughed and continued searching the office. The only thing we thought would be interesting reading was a file box in the desk. It had "Confidential Informants" written on it. Stanley stuffed the cards from it in his shirt and we left the office.

In the short hallway we could see smoke rolling out the open doorways of the Parole Board offices. One convict ran past us into the investigator's office and splashed dry cleaning fluid on everything. We stood and watched as he lit a book of matches and threw it on the desk. The whole room went up in a flash of flames. We watched the fire in the Parole Board offices consume the files and papers on the table and the fiber board ceiling above. It was fascinating to see all this sacred state authority being burned. We leisurely strolled by the open doorways of the burning offices and sauntered down the steps laughing and congratulating each other on what we had found and taken. Stanley was saying something behind me about the value of the watch he'd taken when I reached that bottom step to find the grill bar gate shut and locked. I rattled it a couple times only to find how solidly locked it was. Realizing I couldn't open the gate, I shouted to passing convicts running by to find the switch in the control center and unlock this door. I wasn't sure where the switch was located but nevertheless, no one slowed down or even acknowledged me standing there with my arms waving through the bars. "It's hopeless," I told Stanley. "We can't get out this way." I looked around at the walls in the narrow stairwell we stood in; they were all paneled wood. I shook my head in self-disdain. While we were rummaging in the investigator's office with theft on our mind, others were setting fires around us to everything that would burn. This whole area would eventually burn and we were trapped in the middle of a well-fueled fire. We had to find a way out fast and I scrambled past Stanley saying, "Come on man, we gotta find a way out upstairs." We rushed up the stairway in near panic. At the top we turned to the right where a fire exit sign glowed through the smoke-filled hallway. The door was solid plate steel and locked. I pushed on the bar but it must have been locked from the other side. Turning from that door we raced down the hallway, shutting the doors to the burning offices, thinking this would give us some time. The building was made of poured concrete, but the offices were partitioned with wooden walls and wooden doors and it wouldn't be long until it all burned. The smoke made it difficult to breath, but it was the fire that had me afraid. I jerked open a metal door only to find it to be a mop closet with a sink and boxes on the floor. I moved on down to the end of the short hallway and found a steel set of double doors that led back in the direction of the prison center. These double doors were locked and I could see movement through the small wire glass windows in each door. Beyond the double doors convicts were running from room to room in the case manager's offices. I rattled the doors and they were loose fitting into the jam. This was the only way out and I backed up a couple steps and let fly a right-footed kick into the center between both doors. The doors just shook and I kicked again. I tried to breath through my nose but the smoke was too thick so I held my cap over my mouth and nose and kept kicking. After three or four kicks I'd turn to see how far along the fire had gotten. It was licking through the walls in some places in the Parole Board offices. I could feel the heat rising and kept kicking just above the lock on the door thinking that was the weak spot. The fear mounting in my mind only made me redouble my kicking, driving my right foot into that spot, hopping back and driving it in hard again. At some point I stopped to cough and wheeze. Stanley came up behind and in a muffled voice he said, "Here, take this, put it on." He handed me a military-style gas mask. He'd found them in the mop closet and I immediately pulled it over my face and head. I took a couple of clear breaths and attacked the doors with fresh energy. I'd kept turning around to see how close the fire was. It had completely engulfed the far door to the Parole Board offices and was starting to burn up the wall from the floor just behind us. Stanley was standing on my left. I kept kicking, backing up, and kicking with as much force as I had. Then as I kicked again, the glass on the right door broke and the door started to buckle. I could feel a wave of heat on my back and I kept kicking. And kept kicking until I had the right door open. I had kicked it open opposite the way it was intended to open. When we walked through the doorway I looked back at the fire that had eaten its way across the ceiling. It looked like a tunnel of fire. I noticed also that I had torn the sole of my right boot in kicking on the door. It made a flapping noise as I trudged behind Stanley into a hallway that ran between the caseworkers' offices. All these offices were in full flame on both sides of us. We had to bolt past the open doors where flames billowed out. Every time I touched the walls to feel my way along, the heat forced me to the center of the hallway. We finally made it to the stairway and down in between the grill bar gates around the control center. I glanced backward into the hallway where the secretary and deputy warden offices were. They were all blazing. It looked like something I'd once read in a book describing hell. Fire and smoke bellowed out one office door then another, almost as if the fire was keeping time to the crackling and popping noises. All it needed was a little red man with horns and tail to jump out and raise his arms like a maestro.

With Stanley in the lead I lumbered behind with the distinct flap-flap gait of a near cripple. In the long hallway again convicts continued to run in both directions. Stanley said something about the hospital and as we got closer, I could see convicts running out of the pharmacy door carrying boxes. The hospital had been cracked like a $1 million egg. Just inside the doorway two convicts were lying on the floor with that content, complacent look on their faces. One of them still had a needle stuck in his arm. We wandered down the short corridor between examination rooms, doctor's offices, and dentist's offices. Everything was trashed, large wire glass windows were beaten out. The desk drawers in the doctor's offices were wrenched out and scattered around the room. The dentist's chair was laying in the rubble of broken and bent tools and attachments. All the cabinets were standing open empty, the contents strewn around the room like a storm had hit the place. At the pharmacy door there were small cardboard boxes scattered everywhere. I picked up one empty box and on it, printed in bold black letters, it read: "Morphine Sulfate-Liquid, 50 vials. I dropped it and looked at another box that read: "Demerol Liquid-50 vials." There must be seven or eight of the empty boxes with an assortment of class "A" drugs stenciled across the sides. Stanley pulled open the pharmacy door and we looked in at the scene. One convict was bent over at a sink gagging and puking. There were empty vials and used syringes scattered across the countertop. Other small cardboard boxes lay empty on the floor with three other convicts who were blue from death from overdosing themselves. Two other convicts stood at the counter completely absorbed in the needles they were injecting into their arms. Stanley pushed the door closed and said, "This is like a candy store for kids." I stood there wondering why all these heavy-duty drugs were kept in a prison hospital. We turned and legged our way back to the hallway and toward our living area.

The noise level had gone down considerably from what it was an hour ago. There weren't as many people running the hallway. It was as if everything that could be burned was on fire and everything that could be broken lay shattered where they were found. Water came from broken pipes in at least two dozen places in our hike from the hospital to Cellhouse 2. It was like a lull period in the eye of a hurricane. As if everyone was holding their breath for something to come.

When we reached Cellhouse 2, it was also relatively quiet from what it had been; there was some movement but without the convulsive exuberance that rocked the senses just a little while ago. Stanley made comment about it and I didn't understand the change either. We continued our ambling pace down the tier to our cells and intended resting place. We almost made it when I heard Shorty shout from behind us to come help Omar. We both spun around to see Shorty about six or seven cells away waving and saying something about "come quick."

I stepped out in his direction but Stanley kinda lagged back hesitating, only 'cuz he didn't like Shorty. He believed Shorty to be a blow-hard braggart. When I reached

Shorty he was standing in front of Omar's cell door. I pulled open the door and saw Omar in the semi-darkness laying on his bed. I stood in the door for a second or two, quietly calling Omar's name a couple times, then slowly edged toward him. Just as I reached the bed Stanley came in saying "What's going on?" and flipped on the light switch. I was startled by all the blood splattered on the cell walls and in puddles under my feet. Omar was laying on his side facing the wall. I hesitated for a moment 'cuz he looked to be breathing. Then I gripped his shoulder and rolled him on his back. He immediately started fighting and thrashing, trying to turn back on his side. I couldn't help but notice that his throat was torn open. When I released his shoulder he rolled back facing the wall. I stood there kinda in shock, my mind not accepting what my eyes were seeing. I turned to Shorty and then Stanley and said in a wavering whisper, "What the hell is this about?" I turned back to Omar and thought we got to get him some help fast. Then I remembered about the front being blocked by fire. I heard Stanley question Shorty behind me. "Who did this?" he demanded. I leaned over the bed to look closer at Omar's face and the wound on his throat. I heard Shorty swear that he didn't know anything. The wound wasn't just a single cut, but as if his attacker(s) had concentrated five or six slashes at his wind pipe. Raw flesh hung out of the wound and moved with a wet, sucking sound every time he breathed in or out. Medically, I couldn't do anything for him. Then as I watched helplessly he started to cough and spew blood from his mouth and throat. He shuddered for about 10 seconds and quit breathing. I rolled him on his back again. His eyes were open but only the white could be seen. Small bloody bubbles were popping at his throat as that last breath slipped from his lungs. I continued to stand above him looking at him in death. I knew Omar; I liked him. Then Shorty pushed by me and started heaving up and down on Omar's chest but all that did was bring out more bloody froth. He gave up after seeing the futility. Stanley started questioning him again about who he saw near Omar's cell. Omar was well liked by most everyone, I thought. He had made parole and was just waiting for the paperwork to be released. He told everyone at the beginning of the riot that he wouldn't participate because he was waiting on that paperwork to go home. The question kept ringing in my head—Why? He wasn't a rat or an informer. He always showed respect and was respected by all. Shorty kept denying knowledge to Stanley's questions. I thought, could it be because he refused to join the madness of the riot? Could it have been an old unsettled argument? That last thought made me shift gears. If this could happen to Omar, then it could happen to any of us. We all had enemies in here, known enemies and unknown ones. In prison it's always safer to be a little paranoid. I was angry at having to watch a friend die and angry at myself for being so reckless the last few hours. I turned to Stanley and said, "Come on, he doesn't know anything," and marched out of Omar's cell. Stanley followed me out on the tier and I told him in an exasperated tone, "What in the hell have we been doing running around in all this bullshit without anything to protect ourselves?" He just looked at me without saying anything. I'm sure he knew what was running at neck-breaking speed through my mind. We had to arm ourselves. We passed our cells and marched into the TV room. I hopped up on the picnic table that I'd played cards on just hours earlier. There were four other convicts in the room but they were engrossed in shooting drugs that they had and didn't pay us any attention.

Stanley and I worked in the prison industry area. From time to time we had brought in knives we'd made on the job and we'd stashed them in the false ceiling behind the lighting fixture above the table.

Standing on the tabletop, I twisted out the four-foot long fluorescent bulbs from the fixture and handed them to Stanley. After pushing the fixture back into the hollow of the ceiling, I took one of the long bulbs to scrape the pieces of steel toward the opening. This didn't work and I grabbed onto the edge of the fixture opening and swung off the table. Then with Stanley's added weight, an eight-foot piece of fiber board ceiling crashed down on the floor with our fabricated knives. We gathered them up, ignoring the stares from the druggies across the room. We had four knives apiece and now we were ready for whatever. My paranoia had leveled off and I actually felt better with a knife in easy reach. I thought back on the few hassles I'd had with other convicts over the years. I knew I'd been real lucky in the last couple hours. I shook off the thoughts of Omar and what had probably caused his death. We left the TV room and went into Stanley's cell. He took a roll of gray duct tape out of his jacket pocket and used it to fashion handles on our sharpened pieces of steel. We sat in his cell for about 30 minutes working on them. We discussed our next move and decided we should check out Cellhouse 1 for John and the other friends we'd split up with. Before leaving, I snatched my jacket out of my cell and we headed across the long hallway into Cellhouse 1.

Tramping into the cellblock I noticed a group of convicts gathered around the bathroom door. They were watching as another convict was breaking the porcelain commodes and sinks. He had a 3½-foot piece of pipe or tool of some kind. We stopped to watch him swing and shatter the mirrors above the sinks. For some reason I wanted that pipe. I told Stanley to watch my back and pushed through the audience around the door. In a muffled voice I asked the guy with the pipe what he thought he was accomplishing by breaking all this and pointed around the room with a knife in my hand. He had a startled expression on his face and said that he was just having fun. I told him that I wanted that pipe in his hand, pointing at it with my knife. He looked puzzled at that and his face melted in fear when I took two steps toward him. He looked at my knife and at the gas mask over my face and when I brought up my empty left hand he backed away. I told him again that I wanted his pipe. He stammered something about not wanting any trouble and reached out to gently place the end of the pipe in my empty left hand. I grasped onto the pipe, turned and stalked out of the wrecked bathroom with my boot flapping like a flat tire. Stanley was the only convict at the door when I brushed by. I heard him chuckle a couple times when he fell in step with me on my way to John's cell.

John lived on the bottom floor of the cellblock. This is a kind of honor or merit block. When we reached his cell door we just walked right in. Boots, Weasel, and John looked up as we came in the door. They asked and we told them about our bit of adventure. John described the front lobby as wrecked and on fire when they left the area. Stanley told them about Omar and as he described how we'd found him, I used the tape to lash the pipe to my right hand, making it an effective extension of my arm and an excellent weapon. It was some sort of tool with threads on one end and a fist-size knot on the other end. Taped to my hand it was like a 3½-foot mace.

I continued to listen as the discussion centered on what we should do next. John said we could covey up in his cell and he demonstrated by showing us how his cell door locked and unlocked with a twist of a small knob on the inside of the door. All the cells in this honor block had deadbolt locks that could be operated from inside the cell. John stood by the door and said he thought we should get out before the State Police stormed the place. He said he'd seen some convicts leave by way of the front gate while they were exploring the lobby. The officials were letting convicts who wanted out of the riot to turn themselves in at the front fence. So all we had to do was get out of the prison building. Our options were discussed—those being only two. Either stay in John's cell until the cops came in or find a way out now. I didn't feel good about staying inside and agreed with John that we should find a way out. It was agreed that John, Boots, and Weasel would go in one direction; Stanley and I would check the basement and maintenance area and we'd all meet back in John's cell in one hour.

I gave Weasel and Boots a knife apiece and I kept two. Stanley gave John two of his knives. With everyone armed we felt a lot better. I thought to myself that if anyone gets within reach of my pipe, they better hope I know them and trust them. I tapped my pipe against the cell wall and it was solid and deadly.

Just before leaving the cell, I taped my right boot to stop the sole from flapping. With everyone and everything ready, Stanley and I left first.

3   Searching for a Way Out

Stepping out of the cell I noticed right off that the cellblock was deserted. Not a soul but us left inside. I imagined everyone else had already gotten out. The tinny sound of a radio from upstairs somewhere singing something about "Slip-sliding away." It fit so well with what I was feeling about then. We had jacked around too long and the cops were gonna storm in there any minute. We had to find a way out before they came in. I had images of the State Police shooting everyone they found inside. I'd read about the indiscriminate killing they'd done in retaking the Attica Prison in New York. Stanley said there was a way out through the basement. I knew how to get there, but I wasn't sure of exactly where.

The single lightbulb overhead in the center of the cellblock shined down through the smoke like a lone flashlight in the fog. It gave everything a hazy gray color. But it couldn't penetrate the walls of darkness at the front of the block.

We moved past the closed cell doors and into the water that covered the floor at the front of the cellblock. It flowed from the bathroom door in a steady stream.

With Stanley in the lead, we crept up to the open gate to the hallway. He took the right side of the opening and I the left. We made our way out into a small vestibule, a guard post with a lock box that controls the cell doors and a name roster of the convicts assigned to the cellblock. I kept low and close to the wall, bringing my pipe up for anything unexpected, and stepped past the portal into the long corridor.

Whipping my head back and forth I could see nothing but darkness and smoke in either direction. I quickly stepped over beside Stanley and he started down the corridor toward the center of the joint.

All the overhead lights had been busted out and the only illumination came in through the windows from the perimeter fences. The windows are spaced about 15 feet apart. It looked like thick slices of bright light cutting across the width of the hallway. It gave the moving gray smoke an eerie glow. We stayed close to the wall and ducked under each window moving in a slow, steady pace.

We met a flowing stream of water and it seemed to cover the entire floor with each step we took. I thought I could hear movement ahead and when we passed the chow hall doorway, I could distinctly hear the sound of water spraying inside.

Moving on, it got even darker. We were near the center of the joint, the chow hall on our left and the gym on our right. There weren't any windows in this part of the hallway and I crept along with my shoulder against the wall to guide me.

At the opening to the gym doors Stanley stopped and I moved up behind him. We could definitely hear movement ahead of us; it sounded like something heavy being moved. I tilted my head slightly to locate the direction of the noise, but the closed-in confines of this section of the hallway gave the noise a deceptive hollow echo. I heard Stanley mumble, "Come on!" And he crossed the opening, passing the gym doors with me just a step behind.

A sudden defiant shout ripped the darkness and we both pressed ourselves against the wall. Just ahead of us black silhouetted shapes moved together and a loud scream reverberated around us. More shapes rushed forward through the smoke struggling with others. It looked like we had wandered onto the back side of an ambush.

I felt Stanley grab my right sleeve and pull me sideways past the still-smoldering captain's office.

Then there was more shouting and dark shapes ran by us in the direction from which we'd come. So far we hadn't been seen or we'd just been ignored. The fighting was in the front and back of us now.

Stanley pulled me into the next doorway where thick, black smoke poured out. I couldn't see anything, but I knew we were in the stairwell that led to the basement. I moved backwards, watching and listening to the battle going on in the hallway.

At the stairs, I felt my way down the first flight completely blinded by the smoke that came up from below. Water ran from step to step at my feet. And making the turn down the second flight, I could see where the smoke curled over the archway into the stairway from the basement.

On reaching the bottom we stepped off into about four inches of water that had accumulated across the whole basement floor. Amazingly, most of the smoke stayed close to the ceiling, leaving about five feet of clear space to see through. I had to hunch over to get below the thick smoke. We turned to the right and moved toward the laundry.

The basement held the prison laundry, clothing issue, a small garment factory, and prison maintenance shops. There was a long hallway that ran under the entire prison, just under the hallway above. Stanley mumbled through his mask that the exit was on the other side of the maintenance shop and he trudged on through the water in the lead.

Moving past the windows into clothing issue I could see the stacks of prison clothes burning on the shelves. On past the garment factory and it was in full flame. I could feel the heat, even through the thick wire glass. At the opening that led into the laundry, Stanley hesitated and looked back at me. "It's on fire!" he said in an astonished tone. I stepped up beside him and he pointed down the short interconnected hallway saying, "Maintenance is just on the other side of the laundry, but look

. . . it's on fire." All I could see was a tunnel of flames coming out of the garment factory on the left and out of the laundry on the right. To get to the maintenance we had to pass through the laundry, but there was no way we could get past those flames. I waved my arm at the fires, "Is there another way to get in there?" I asked. He just shook his head and backed away from the intense, glowing heat. I noticed the number of empty, plastic bottles of dry-cleaning fluid floating in the water at our feet. "Are there any other exits down here?" I asked. He turned to the left and then to the right as if to get his bearings and said, "I only worked here for a couple of months and that one through the laundry is the only one I know about.

As we talked we made our way down the hallway, away from the fire. Surely there are other avenues to get out from down here. I also wasn't in too big of a rush to go back up those stairs just yet either. We passed through two unlocked gates and toward a solid steel door. It had a sign painted on the door in big letters, "Off Limits." Moving closer and up a ramp that looked like it was for wheelchairs, I noticed the banging, pounding noise. I'd heard it for the last three or four minutes that we'd been down here. Unconsciously, we had been drawn to the sound and followed it to this steel door. Someone on the other side of that door was beating the hell out of something. The door was shut but it wasn't locked.

"Come on, I said. "Maybe it's a way out." And I toed the door open and stepped inside. As the door swung back we froze, just staring around the dark room.

Directly in front of us, about 30 feet away, a huge steel globe-like structure sat in the middle of the floor. From the bright lights inside the globe I could see five or six people mouthing silent screams through the thick glass window facing us. Off to our right there were two guys standing at a panel of red and green flashing buttons. The noise we originally heard came from another guy pounding on a steel cabinet hung on the wall. It looked like a pipe wrench that he was using. Watching the guys at the podium of flashing buttons, they were taking turns, pushing one button, then another. Then they'd spin around to see what affect it had on those in the globe. It sounded like fans switching on and off with each group of buttons they pushed. Looking closer at the globe, it had a big door on the side, like one of those diving bells that I'd seen in underwater movies. There was a shiny spoke wheel in the center of the door to seal it shut. I just stood there in shock realizing that it was the state's infamous gas chamber. I turned my head to the left and in the gloom could see the row of death cells. It all looked so menacing. Glancing back at the guys in the globe I didn't know any of them. Then one of the guys at the panel of buttons hollered at us, "Do you guys know how to work this?" He indicated the flashing panel. Stanley and I just shook our heads. And he went on in a rush saying, "We're gonna gas those fuckin' rats in there and you guys can help if you want." We continued shaking our heads "no" without saying anything. Then the guy pounding on the cabinet quit his assault and shouted, "I got it!" and pulled the cabinet doors open. The two guys at the panel rushed over to see what he'd found. At that moment I grabbed Stanley's arm and hauled him backwards through the door, pulling the door shut behind me. I didn't want to be around if and when they found the cyanide crystals and acid. We scooted back down the incline, splashing our way back past the burning shops and to the stairs.*

Knowing what was waiting in the hallway upstairs, we inched from step to step, listening, but only hearing the gurgle of water running at our feet. At the top of the stairwell we moved to the open doorway and stood listening for a moment. Nothing. It was as quiet as a tomb. We quickly stepped out into the hallway and put our backs to the wall. I had my pipe up and ready to swat at anyone who came near.

Looking at Stanley behind me, he had a knife in each hand. I said in a low voice, "We should check out that door at the end of the hallway. Hell, it might be open." Stanley said, "Yeah, we've still got 40 minutes before we meet the others at the cell."

Keeping my back to the wall I slowly side-stepped along while trying to see through the blackness. Hearing a noise, I froze, but kept going when I realized it came from behind us further down the hallway. The only other identifiable sound is the flip-splash of my shoes where the tape had come loose. We had edged along about 30 yards and I literally ran into the stacked bed frames and tables turned on their sides. This was some sort of barricade thrown up across the width of the corridor. We had to move out into the center of the hallway to find the opening through it. Stanley stayed on my left so as not to get hit if anyone came at us. I kept swinging the pipe back and forth to kinda feel my way through the smoke and darkness. Once past the obstruction we moved to the hallway wall again to guide us.

At the control center gates we couldn't even consider going out through the front of the prison. The flames gave the whole area a red glow. Those fires in the outer offices are gonna be burning for a while. We kept going on and, for some reason, the smoke wasn't as thick. Then we were out of the windowless part of the hallway and once again light from the outside fence guided us along.

At the first window I stopped at hearing a rumbling sound. Looking out I could see large Army trucks pulling into the parking lot just on the other side of the double fence. It wasn't a comforting sight to see arriving National Guard troops. We had to get out of that building before they could muster enough forces out there to storm in.

Moving on I saw that familiar red glow ahead and through the haze and smoke, I could see the flames gushing out of the psychological unit. It was a two-floor structure. On the first floor, convicts received psychotherapy. A barn-like edifice with fancy wood-paneled offices, plush, comfortable couches to sit on, and carpeting running throughout. A pleasant, homey-type atmosphere when having your head shrunk by therapists. On the second floor was a housing unit for the older, feeble, and partially insane convicts.

We crossed the hallway opposite the blaze to get by but the heat was searing and we couldn't get within 60 feet of the unit entrance. Flames shot out halfway across the hallway width. I could see the charred wall and ceiling where the gulfing flames roared out. After numerous attempts to get closer, we gave up and turned back the way we'd come.

---

* The events Rolland describes as having taken place in and around the gas chamber during the riot were never reported, or even rumored, during the official investigation or by investigative journalists following the riot in 1980. Rolland is aware of that, but stands firmly by his account of these events as detailed here.

I stepped over to one of the hallway windows to see if there were any old men in that upstairs dorm. The entire bottom floor was burning and I couldn't see any of the dorm windows through the billowing smoke. For a split second I thought I saw someone standing in one of the windows, but I couldn't be sure as the smoke blew across the spot and completely covered the upper floor of the structure. Backing away, all I could do was hope those old guys got out.

We continued on and passed the open gates at the control center. Unless the other guys found a way out, we were stuck 'cuz every avenue out was blocked at that end of joint. At least the cops wouldn't be able to get in until the fires burned out. Sliding over to the right side of the hallway we crept on until voices ahead stopped us.

Taking a few steps at a time, we moved ahead until the dappled shapes of two guys appeared out of the darkness and whirling smoke. They stood in a doorway facing each other, talking adamantly about someone inside. Stanley mumbled in my ear, "That's the guard's chow hall. We can get into the kitchen from there." I knew immediately what he was referring to. At the back of the kitchen there are doors that lead out.

Then the two guys disappeared from view and we moved to the door. Stanley went in first and I followed, stepping onto the carpeted floor of the guard's cafeteria, a medium-sized room for probably 12 tables. The drop ceiling and wood decor gave the immediate impression of walking into a restaurant. Most of the overhead lighting hung shattered on strands of wire. I followed Stanley between tables and overturned chairs. Off to the left I saw the two guys we'd seen at the door. They had their backs to us talking to another guy kneeling over what looked like a body. I heard one say, "Is he dead?" I recognized the gravelly voice answering, "No, not yet, but we got to help him!" I hesitated for a few more steps, then turned in their direction. As I got closer I knew it was Frank. He was on his knees beside a body in bloody long johns. It had to be a guard because convicts weren't allowed to have long john underwear.

I asked Frank, "What's going on man?" He turned and just stared at me. I knew him from our discussion about Vietnam. He had been a medic in the army. Although he was mostly a loner in there, our being vets gave us a mutual friendship. Moving closer for a better look, I pulled my gas mask off and Frank said, "Maaan, I'm glad to see ya. We gotta help the guard or he's gonna die." I stared down at the body of Captain Vasquez. I glanced back at Frank saying, "We're trying to find a way out. Do you know if the back doors to the kitchen are locked?" Frank shook his head and said, "That way has been blocked for over an hour." He turned back to the guard and said, "If we let any of these guards die, it's gonna be a lot worse than it was before." He wiped blood off the Captain's face with a towel. His head had long gashes across it and it looked broken. Then Frank rolled him on his side. The Captain moaned and started pleading in syllables that couldn't be understood. I just stared as he tried to talk through smashed lips and a jaw cocked to the side. It had to be broken.

I turned and waived for Stanley to come over. He trudged between the table and around the other side of Frank and the Captain. I said to him, "You know Frank, he says we can't get through the kitchen and he wants us to help with the Captain." Stanley just shrugged his shoulders. As I saw it, we would be helping Frank because

I didn't care one way or the other about the guard. He had gone out of his way to make my time harder and I couldn't feel sorry for a dog that made his career out of biting me. But Frank made a good point, we couldn't let any of these guards die regardless of how we felt about them.

Frank tried to straighten the Captain's legs and roll him over. Then when he got him over, I saw his hands. They were handcuffed behind his back. Frank said, "I need a handcuff key. Do you guys have a key?" I backed toward the door and said, "I know where there's probably a bunch of them." I turned and passed the two guys we'd seen at the door and headed out into the hallway for the control center.

At the control center I crawled through the broken window and went directly to a Peg-Board on the wall that was full of key rings. I found what I needed, stuck it in my pants pocket and crawled back out. I made it back to the guard's chow hall in less than five minutes.

As soon as I walked I noticed two new fellows with the two others we first saw. One of the new guys stood over Frank with a claw hammer in his right hand. The other three had an assortment of weapons and they all had their backs to me. I hesitated just inside the doorway—watching, listening. The guy with the hammer said, "He's our hostage and we're taking him." I didn't know any of these guys but, I could tell from his voice inflections that the one guy talking was a Chicano. Stanley still stood on the other side of Frank facing the group demanding the guard and he didn't show it but, I knew he saw me. Frank started to say something to the guy with the hammer but before he could get the words out the guy swung the hammer and in one motion, hit Frank on the side of the head. Frank pitched over the guard's legs. It happened so fast and unexpected. I just charged forward and caught the first guy closest to me in the head with my pipe as he tried to turn. Stanley hopped over the prostrate bodies of Frank and the guard and slammed into the Chicano that hit Frank. He had turned to face me when Stanley put both knees in his back. The other two guys broke and ran into the kitchen area.

The guy I'd hit went down like a sack of rocks and didn't move. Stanley had the guy with the hammer down and they were struggling on the floor. I moved over and hit the arm holding the hammer, knocking it out of his hand. Then I smacked him in the head and when Stanley rolled away, I cracked him a couple more good licks for hitting Frank.

Stanley had Frank sitting up when I got over to him. He was conscious and we hauled him to his feet, walked him over to the lights around the serving line and had a look at his head. Blood trickled out of his nose and left ear. A large, blood-engorged knot poked through his hair above the ear. It looked bad and Frank saw the expression on my face and gingerly raised his hand, touching the knot with his finger. He said, "Help me over to the sink."

While Stanley supported him around the serving line, I kept watch for anyone that came in. Mainly I kept an eye on the kitchen door waiting on those two who ran to pump their nuts up and come back.

Frank ran some water and washed his face. He said, "As long as my ear bleeds freely and I don't pass out, then it should be alright." He held onto the countertop and came out from behind the serving line holding a wet rag to his head. He said, "You guys are gonna have to keep me awake 'cuz I might not wake up. Shit it hurts." I sauntered over to him and said, "You ain't gotta worry about that 'cuz I don't think any of us is gonna get any sleep for a while." He laughed and pushed off from the counter, walking on shaky legs toward the Captain. Stanley followed him and Frank slumped down in a chair next to the Captain. He pulled the rag away from his head, looked expectantly at it and dropped it on the floor. Then he looked over at me and said, "Did you get that handcuff key?" It floored me. Here he was hurt, and probably had a cracked skull, and he still wanted to help this guard. "Yeah," I said and I ambled over and handed him the key ring.

I stood over him while he got down on his knees again and rolled the Captain over. The Captain groaned as if he was being disturbed in sleep and I got a look at his wrists. The cuffs looked like they'd been stomped on. In places they had cut through the skin and Frank had to push the meat back to get the bloody cuffs off.

With that done Frank sat the Captain up, holding him by his shoulders. Frank asked him three or four times, "Can you walk?" but got no response. I moved around behind the Captain and looked down at the top of his head. He had one of those short burr haircuts and I could see blood welling from the long gashes from his forehead to his crown. Frank kept wiping the blood off his face and out of his eyes and talking to him. Something serious is busted inside this guard's head. He acted oblivious to us or to his wounds.

"We should take him to one of the cells," I said to Frank. I explained how the doors in Cellblock 1 locked from the inside. We could hide the Captain in one of them. Frank immediately agreed and we made the guard ready to move him.

The hallway was quiet and while Stanley and Frank carried the Captain, I kept watch and guided us through the obstacles, darkness, and smoke. We didn't see anyone else on the trip back to the cellblock. Stanley and I waited outside the cell while Frank gave the Captain first aid as best as he could.

While we waited, the other three in our group showed up. They were breathing hard as if they'd been running and they'd been in a fight. John had a long cut across his back. It looked bad. I asked Weasel what happened. When he started to explain, John interrupted with fear-laced statements, "We're all gonna die in here! They won't let us out!" The way he spoke gave me those hackles of paranoia at the back of my neck. I tried to listen to what Weasel was saying. They had checked all the dorms and at the school they'd found a way out but it was being guarded by other convicts and that's where they had gotten jumped. John kept interrupting with, "There's no way out, we're gonna die . . ." And four or five other excited, high-pitched squeaks of panic-fear. Stanley immediately grabbed John's arm and pulled him away from the rest of us. He put his arm around John's shoulder and told him to calm down, that everything was gonna be alright. I saw the look in Stanley's eyes as he consoled John. My heart was racing in the panic I felt. Weasel went on to describe the ambush they'd walked into. I felt my knees shake at seeing the fear on the faces around me. When I looked over at Boots he said in a shaky voice, "They took our knives and told us not to try leaving again."

Then Frank came out of the cell and jumped right into telling me what I've gotta do for the Captain. "You got to keep him awake." He pulled a handful of yellow pills from his shirt pocket and tried to hand them to me saying, "Give him a couple of these Meth-tabs every couple hours and don't let him sleep." I started shaking my head no and I refused to take the pills. Finally I said, "Wait a minute, I'm not gonna be responsible for or babysit a half-dead guard. No, it's not my responsibility." This idea of watching over the guard and my friends being in an ambush was coming at me too fast. Frank said, "Man, you gotta help me with this." He went on to explain the obvious about our situation, what would happen if we let this guard die. As he explained, I thought about how I could justify my actions in refusing. Also, what if someone wanted to kill him? How could I justify stopping them? What if the cops found me in a cell with him? And why should I care what happens to this dog? I continued shaking my head and Frank kept lecturing and then he started describing the Captain's wounds. I shook my head in amazement at the graphic detail. "He's been stabbed in numerous places in the back and chest, can't tell if his lungs are punctured. His right arm is broken at the elbow. Both his wrists are crushed and ribs feel broken. His jaw is broken and he has a concussion with very probable breaks in his skull. He's been sodomized repeatedly with something." I kept shaking my head but I accepted the pills that Frank offered. He stepped back to the cell and I followed him on in.

The Captain lay on his back, staring up from the bed. His head was a swath of bandages as well as his chest and arms. I noticed the bloody long johns in the corner on the floor. He had a blank look in his eyes and his face had started to swell. I just stood looking at the Captain. I asked Frank, "Are you gonna stay with us to help with him?" I turned to see Frank staring into the mirror at the lump in his head. He said, "I'll stay with you guys a while, but there's a lot of hurt people in here." I thought about that for a couple seconds and said, "We'll find him some prison clothes, make sure he stays awake and we can wait it out here and no one will be the wiser." Frank just nodded his head and continued examining himself in the mirror.

I trudged out of the cell and told everyone that I'll be staying with Frank and the guard. Boots and Weasel said they'd stay. Stanley agreed to stay but he wanted to continue looking for a way out. John didn't say anything. Every time I made eye contact with him he'd look away as if he was embarrassed for showing so much fear earlier. I told him he should let Frank look at the cut on his back. That seemed to relieve some of the awkwardness he felt and he went on into the cell.

It was agreed that we should move the Captain to the second tier. Water was already running into the cells on the first floor. We hauled the Captain on a blanket up the stairs and into an empty, dry cell.

It had gotten light outside. From the cell window we could hear and see more National Guard arriving in full force. There is no mistaking that familiar wind-whipping sound of helicopters passing overhead and landing outside the fences.

Someone came through the cellblock shouting that a meeting was being held in the gym. That had been more than an hour ago but no one in our group wanted to attend. It sounded like a trap to me and I didn't like the idea about being in a crowd of strangers. For some reason we thought we could be independent from what's going on outside this cell. But then, we couldn't get out the madness so the next best thing for us to do was hide.

Getting settled in the cell wasn't a problem. Stanley taped a piece of towel over the small window in the door, and with the door locked, our little refuge felt secure.

I passed out the last of my cigarettes and we smoked and tried to relax. John started the conversation speculating on what was gonna happen next. "Nothing's gonna happen," I said, "except when it gets daylight, I think the cops are gonna come back in. And I think we should stay right here until they do." This opened the door for everyone to speak their mind and everyone gave a different variation of what was to come. Stanley said we should rush the school building in force and get the hell out of here. John agreed that we should get out but "I'm not going back into that school building!" he said in a shaky voice. Frank stood up from the edge of the bed and told everyone, "You already know they're stopping everyone from leaving. We're in this for the long haul and you all better get used to it."

We sat for hours coming up with different plans of what we should do. I kept moving to the door every time I heard someone pass on the tier. I'd pull the towel back and peek out and then let it drop. At this point I didn't know what we could do beyond staying where we were.

4   The Hunt for Food

As daylight came and the morning passed, the anticipated retaking of the joint by the forces outside didn't come. We all kept quiet when we heard anyone passing by the door. No one seemed to pay our hide-out any particular attention and that was fine with us. But as noon dragged by another kind of expectancy and restlessness set in on the cocked ears and darting eyes at the cell door.

John mumbled something about food. "It's been years," he said, "since I've missed two meals in the same day." I glanced over at him, not saying anything. But I sure wasn't thinking about food. He seemed to be coming out of his panic conniption from earlier. I sat leaning against the small wash basin near the door. Everyone sat around where they could whisper in subdued voices. The underlying question kept coming up—What are we gonna do?

Weasel sat on the floor by the bed end. He started rummaging through the boxes under the bed. When I asked what he thought he was doing going into the owners property he said, "Ah man, I was hoping whoever lived here would have some coffee or something to eat. I got a bunch of stuff in my locker and I'd sure like a cup of coffee; I ain't had no coffee since yesterday." I thought about that for a couple seconds and said, "We could make a food run. I'd kinda like some coffee myself and we're out of cigarettes." Stanley piped in with, "We just went to the canteen yesterday. I got everything we need in my cell."

It was agreed. John and Boots would stay in the cell with the Captain. The rest of us would make a short trip over to Cellhouse 2 where Stanley and I lived. We'd quickly gather all we needed from our cells and take it back to our hideout. It shouldn't take no more than 10 minutes, at the most.

With Stanley in the lead, we quietly hoofed it down the tier and into the stairwell at the front of the block. There we waited in the darkened shadows and watched the hallway.

We heard movement further down the hallway. It sounded like splashing steps of someone walking in the water. The water had risen about two inches; it covered the entire first floor and as far as we could see in the hallway. When we couldn't hear any-thing, we moved slow and easy across the space between the cellblocks. It was day-light outside, but with the ceiling lights knocked out, the feeble light drifting with the smoke through the windows made the images laying in the hallway that much more ominous. Trash or bodies, I couldn't tell.

Moving up the stairs to the second tier of our cellblock, Stanley and I light-foot-ed it down to our houses and went right in. As soon as I walked in my cell, I knew someone had been there. It had been thoroughly ransacked and everything I'd come for was gone. I stood there for a second just looking at the mess and feeling the anger build and subside. "Well shit . . ." I said out loud and turned for the door. As soon as I stepped out on the tier I saw the expression on Stanley's face and knew he'd been robbed too. I shouldn't be surprised, but I didn't expect anyone to rob our cells in the middle of a riot.

No sweat, there was nothing we could do about it then anyways. We had a fast conference, decided to make the trip to Weasel's locker in Dorm B-1, and started down the tier. We'd taken just a few steps when a group of three convicts came out of a cell between us and the stairway. They were dragging a blanket piled with can-teen items. We saw them first and knew they were the thieves that had robbed our house. They were going from cell to cell, ripping off everyone. One did a doubletake at seeing us, then he bristled and jerked a knife out of his belt.

At that moment another group of six convicts rushed through the cellblock door from the hallway. This group started yelling accusations up at the other three con-victs for robbing cells in Cellhouse 6. Words and threats flew back and forth; then the bigger group on the bottom floor went for the stairs. The three cell robbers took off. They dashed around the end of the tier and past the stairway that the larger group was coming up. They raced past us on the opposite tier across the cellblock with the other group hot on their heels. The slowest robber got tackled and there was a tan-gle of guys on him. A lot of words were shouted in Spanish and English, but the fat cell thief didn't have a chance. He was stabbed in a flurry and kicked through the railing of the tier to the floor below. The other two thieves reached the end of the tier and almost made it to the back stairs where they were caught and had to fight.

We stood in place as spectators. One of the robbers attempted to explain that they had the authority of riot leadership to take those things. They stood their ground with knives drawn, but it made no difference; the larger group had pipes, knives, and wooden pick handles. They waded in with solid, unyielding blows, and flashing steel. One more of the thieves was knocked to the floor, and he had his throat cut before being kicked off the tier to the first floor below. The last standing cell thief backed toward the stairs. He had a large kitchen blade in his hand. He lunged at one of his attackers swinging his knife in an upward slash, missed the intended target and before he could recover, a knife slammed hilt-deep into his right side. He hopped backwards and tried to pull on the knife that was obviously stuck between his ribs. He screamed something in Spanish and charged headlong down the stairs to the bot-tom floor. He continued running the length of the cellblock and out into the hallway. He could be heard in the distance splashing away. No one bothered to chase him. Everyone stood stunned for a moment at that bold move, listening at the fading sound of splashing steps.

We had kinda drifted toward the fighting at the end of the tier. Frank said he knew one of the guys in the larger group. They were now looking at us, wondering where we fit into the scheme of things. They probably thought we were with the cell thieves. In there, cell thieves were treated as informers. Proximity could easily be taken as guilt. No one could be sure who anyone was or where they stood in this situation. They all had masks or towels covering their faces. Everyone in our small group had theirs covered as well. But there was something familiar about a few of the other group facing us and edging closer.

Stanley and I were side by side, closest to the bigger group. The tier we were standing on was only about four feet wide. As they came around the corner of the tier, one of their group asked that universal question, "What's happening man?" The voice sounded vaguely familiar, I'd heard it before. Then Frank surprised us by pushing between Stanley and me and ambled toward the larger group. He said something that I didn't quite hear and pulled the towel away from his face. The speaker in the other group recognized Frank and immediately pulled off his towel wrap. And we all recognized Felix. Everyone in the joint knew him. One of the most respected convicts in that place. He had even played in our poker games. But that had been more than a year ago. He had been on administrative segregation for being suspected of dealing in chiva (heroin). Others in the group uncovered and I knew Lucky and Bear. They were also known throughout the prison population. Knowing these guys was a relief because we sure didn't want to have to fight them.

The tension everyone felt seemed to evaporate further when Felix started talking about the initial stages of negotiating with the officials out front. "As soon as we can get to the front," he said, "we're gonna present our demands!"

It dawned on me that that group with Felix was the qualified leadership to get that madness over with. I wanted to hear more, but Frank and Felix walked toward the TV room with their heads together. I heard Frank say something about the Captain as they walked away.

Lucky asked where we'd gotten our gas masks from. And while Stanley told him about our bit of adventure in the investigator's office, we all strolled into the TV room—the same TV room we'd played cards in the night before.

I walked over to the wall of windows facing out the back of the prison and onto the recreation ball field. I stared at the majority of the convict population that had gotten out in the last nine hours. I saw snowflakes blowing by the windows; it had to be cold out there. Those guys had to be miserable; it looked like they were huddled together in groups for warmth. It was at that moment that I was kinda glad we hadn't found a way out.

Hearing Felix say they had all the hostage guards in Cellhouse 6, I turned away from the windows to listen to his plan for the eventual release of them. Frank had evidently told him about how we had acquired the Captain. The conversation centered on the injuries of those hostages in Cellhouse 6 and Frank let spiel his idea of how we had to protect these hostages. It was decided that due to his injuries, Captain Vasquez would stay where we had him. He'd also be one of the first to be released.

Lucky got everyone's attention by turning the volume up on the television. A commentator's voice said, "This is a live view of Protective Custody at the scene of the New Mexico prison riot." A camera outside the fence had focused on the outside windows of Cellblock 4. The scene on the TV was of images through the opaque glass; two men were holding another man against the windows. A welding torch was brought closer to the head of the man being held. The commentator was steadily explaining the images his audience was seeing. The torch was brought even closer and the images started moving as the one being held was trying to avoid the heat of the flame. Then only flames could be seen as the head was engulfed. The camera stayed on the burning head for a few seconds while the commentator said again, "This is live from the New Mexico prison riot." Everyone in the TV room was silent as the camera panned back and forth across the windows. I'm sure my mouth was hanging open at the bizarre scene we were watching. It was beyond anything I'd ever seen. There was also that weird feeling of watching on TV what I knew was actually happening just down the hallway. I had heard that Protective Custody had been gotten into, but I didn't really believe this would be happening. Lucky brought us back to our reality by saying, "Those ratty bastards deserve whatever they get!" He slapped the off button and the TV went black. Most of us still stared at the blank screen.

Then Stanley said, "Let's split up that pile of groceries," he pointed down the tier where the cell thieves had left the blanket, "since a lot of that stuff is ours!" It was a good reason to get moving again. Frank said he would be back later; he and Felix left for Cellhouse 6. A couple of Felix's crew went with Stanley and Weasel to pick through the pile of potato chips, cookies, and cigarettes. Lucky and I walked across the hallway for Cellhouse 1. He said he wanted to see how badly Captain Vasquez was hurt.

When we reached the cell, Boots opened the door and he was alone with the Captain. He said John had left just before we had gotten there. He said, "John talked about finding a way out. He said he didn't want to wait around for the cops to storm in on us." I wasn't surprised, but then I wouldn't have forced him to stay. He can make his own decisions. Somehow, though, I don't believe John would have liked it any better out on that cold recreation yard.

Stanley and Weasel came in with our share of the food, and coffee was made for everyone. Stanley asked about John, and Boots explained again that he'd left. I watched Lucky try to get some response from the Captain on the bed.

In places, I could see where red had seeped through the bandages around the Captain's head. Lucky sat on the edge of the bed and snapped his fingers in the Captain's face to get a reaction. I said, "He probably hears popping and snapping, but it's not from what you're doing." Lucky continued to talk to him. I looked on and thought back to the few encounters I had with this guard before the takeover. As a Captain, he had always played his part well at being top dog. Looking at him then in that helpless condition, it was hard to see him as my enemy. Sipping my coffee and looking at the blank stare in his eyes, it just didn't seem like hate that I felt for him. Lucky tried to feed him a cookie, but he wouldn't chew it. When I said, "I think his jaw's broken," Lucky stood up and matter-of-factly said, "He'll be with the first hostages we release."

The conversation turned toward the possibility of beginning the negotiations with the officials. Lucky said it would have to start soon and everyone trusted Felix to deal with them. He told us about the meeting in the gym. A list of demands had been made and it was decided then that Felix would present the demands and do the talking for us.

We stood and sat around the cell listening to Lucky explain what had gone on the last couple hours. Everyone seemed to feel better about our situation. At least now we knew what was happening inside the joint and that there actually was an ad hoc leadership working toward ending this madness. But I also believed we were wanting to think that it could end soon and that made us feel better.

The images that kept flashing through my mind were of Omar, those guys locked in the gas chamber, and that of the torch. What the hell was all that for? My legs hurt and my eyes were burning. I just wanted to find a safe place to close my eyes and my mind.

Lucky suggested that we make a trip to Cellhouse 6 and see if maybe we should move the Captain there. From the sounds of what Felix and Lucky had been saying, I thought it might very well be a good idea to stay close to the decisionmakers. I also liked the idea of someone else being responsible for that hurt guard.

Before leaving, I tried to get the Captain to take a couple of the pills I got from Frank. But he kept pushing the pills back out of his mouth with his tongue. Stanley came up with the idea to mash the pills and mix with water. It worked a whole lot better, but I think we got more of the mixture on his chest than we got into his mouth. He didn't seem to have any problem with swallowing. It wasn't unlike feeding an obstinate child.

5   The Look of Compassion

The slow hike to Cellhouse 6 was a new assault on the senses. Lucky led the procession down the right side of the corridor. The barricade that we had encountered earlier was dismantled and scattered against the opposite wall. All the fires we'd seen were now smoldering, smoking hulks of unidentifiable piles. Thick clouds of blue-gray smoke hung like curtains in places where we had to feel our way along. Something noxious is in it; I could smell a faint odor of metal even through my gas mask. Just past the control center there were three bodies laying in crumpled heaps against the wall. As we splashed by, water lapped up against them like small waves in the ocean, making them bob and bump the wall.

Reaching Cellhouse 6, we were waved on in by the two convicts watching the door. We could hear a loud argument in the second tier TV room, and followed Lucky up the stairs. From the top of the stairwell I could see Felix standing on one of the steel picnic tables, listening to the shouting of those on the floor around him. Getting closer, I could make out about 30 guys in the TV room. Someone shouted, "Let him die!" And at the TV room door I heard, "I bet he's faking. He ain't having no heart attack!" At first I didn't know who they were talking about. And one voice rose above the rest saying, "Remember when he shot that one escapee, he didn't have to kill him!" And a loud chorus of "Yeah!" I knew then whom they were referring to. He had summarily executed a convict who was wounded in an escape attempt and laying outside the fence. It was an old, true, repeated tale about Lieutenant Herman Hernandez—a much-feared guard with a big-dog attittude toward convicts.

One of the guys pushed his way to the table and said, "We can't let any of these guards die, regardless of what he done. We can't let him die in here!" And the shouting started again. From the sound of it, the majority wanted to hold him hostage, make him suffer, and let him die. The last speaker in the Lieutenant's defense is drowned out with loud protests and angry threats.

49

I stayed by the doorway of the TV room listening to the ongoing heated exchange. To my right I noticed the cell door open on the end of the tier. I caught a glimpse of Lieutenant Hernandez laying on the bed inside as Frank walked out of the cell. He walked past me with a grim expression on his face and went over to Felix. He said something to him that I couldn't hear above the rumbling drone.

Suddenly Felix shouted for everyone to shut it up. When it got quiet, he told everyone, "It's my decision and we're gonna release him to get medical help!" Saying that, he jumped down off the table and stalked out of the TV room and into the cell where the Lieutenant laid. It wasn't surprising that no one said anything loud enough to oppose his decision. Frank followed him and passing me at the door he said, "Come on, you can help . . ."

I'd never seen anyone have a heart attack. But walking in that cell and seeing that guard gasping for each breath convinced me it was for real. He had one hand pressed into the middle of his chest and a painful expression twisted across his gray-blotched face. Laying naked across the bed, he looked like a hog ready for slaughter. He had to tip the scales at or near 400 pounds.

Very carefully we rolled him on his side and placed two folded blankets under him, rolled him back to get him in the middle, and then Felix went out to get more help. It took eight of us to lift him and haul him out on the tier. There we set him down and made adjustments for a better grip on the blanket ends. He just laid back and moaned and shook like a pile of Jello. Others came out of the TV room to look at him and make suggestions about how we should drop him on the trip to the front. Everyone was set and we started down the tier. At the stairwell we had a bit of a problem making the narrow corner and almost dropped him. The economy in the space provided didn't take into account for hauling a tub o' lard. At the bottom we stepped off into about four inches of flood water. To prevent from stepping on each other's feet, we had to kinda coordinate a lock-step—first with the left, then the right. Felix moved out in front and guided us around the trash and hidden obstacles in the water. At the control center gates we turned left and kept moving. No one said anything. All I could hear was our splashing steps and occasional moan from the guard and laborious breathing from those around me carrying him. Passing the offices of the Deputy Warden and secretaries, all I could see inside were piles of smoking ash. It looked strange because the piles were in the shapes of desks and tables and only about six inches tall. The metal doors to the offices were buckled and melted and looked more like rubber instead of steel. The walls and ceiling in the hallway were still smoking and they were once painted concrete. It was like being in an oven, and in places I could see where chunks of concrete popped loose from the rebar inside. Up ahead was the visiting room and I heard Felix call someone's name. As we moved closer, I could hear him explain that we were bringing a guard through. At the visiting room door, we turned in and amazingly it hadn't been burned too badly. Some of the long tables by the door looked scorched, but nothing like the other offices and rooms in the hallway. We moved on through and out the other end of the visiting room where only visitors usually leave by. And suddenly we were in the lobby. Felix had three of his crew around him and he explained again what we were there for. They were armed to the teeth, obviously to prevent anyone else from sneaking out. We found a dry place to set the guard down. He just laid there oblivious to our effort to haul his big ass. I looked around the lobby. I'd never had the opportunity to see this part of the joint. Felix cautiously eased over to the double doors that led to the front gate. I continued looking around at the destroyed pop machines, candy machines, and coffee machines that lay on their sides. Someone had jammed the eight-foot flag staff with the state flag on it into the glass front of the coffee machine. I looked around for the American flag and wondered how ingenuously disrespected I'd find it, but it was nowhere to be seen. Glancing back toward Felix, he's waving his towel head wrap out the broken glass doors to get the attention of the massed forces at the front gate. It didn't take long. A bullhorn voice shouted, "You waving the rag, come out where we can see you!" Felix looked back at us staying well back from the doors, and boldly pushed the empty door frame open and stepped out onto the concrete stoop. He shouted, "We got a guard in here having a heart attack!" He stood with his back to us whirling his towel around at his side and said, "We're gonna bring him out if you want him!" I tried to see out through the doors, but from where I stood at the back of the lobby, all I could see was the glare of lights shining in through the door. It didn't take them long to decide. That same bullhorn voice yelled, "Bring him out!" Felix turned and waved at us to bring him on. We quickly gathered the ends of the blanket and lifted the dead weight in one motion. I heard Bear behind me say, "Okay fat boy, we're gonna let you go!" It sounded funny, the way he said it, but no one laughed. This guard's too heavy to laugh at and until now, I didn't think about walking out in full view (of what? what's out there?). I was second on the left side of the blanket. Lucky was in front of me and he ain't much cover if they wanted to shoot a little bit. As we moved to the double doors, I had a sudden thought. Maybe we should have put some clothes on this naked bastard. They aren't going to like it that he's butt ass naked. Lucky passed through the door frame and I glanced up from watching his feet. The door frame hit my left shoulder. At the same time I saw the gun tower and front gate. Both bristled with every kind of rifle made and they were all pointed at us. Standing on the stoop Felix said, "Take him to the gate . . ." and we passed him and stepped down the two steps to the sidewalk. I glanced around. The National Guard lined the outside fence as far as I could see to the left and to the right. We kept in step down the sidewalk of no-man's-land and I looked up at the tower above us. It had at least 20 cops in it and they all hung out the flip-up windows with rifles, following our every step. Off to the right I could see some women and TV cameras behind the National Guard and they were all watching us. As we got closer to the gate I recognized the Warden, Deputy Warden, Captain Nunez, and five to six other top dogs of this asylum. Again, that same bullhorn voice above us in the tower shouted, "Leave him at the gate and move back inside the building!" Yeah, right, like we thought we'd try to carry this greaseball all the way to the hospital. It amazes me how guards love to hear their own voices. That one with the bullhorn will go home tonight and tell his wife how he told us to leave his hurt buddy at the gate and how we followed his every uttered word. We sat him on the walkway real easy like and folded the blanket ends to cover him. His eyes were still squeezed shut and he huffed and puffed like a fat fish out of water. The weight on this guard and the stress of being in the hands of those he's abused is what's tripping his heart out. I took one last look at him and followed Bear back toward the lobby doors. I could hear voices behind me saying, "Who is it, who is it?" and the squeak of wheels of the cart they were pushing to the gate to load him on. We didn't bother to open the door frames, just ducked under the cross bar and stepped through the empty frames. The glass crunched under my feet as I moved through and into the welcome darkness of the lobby. Felix came in behind us and we stood in the darkened shadows to watch the white-suited medics take the patient out. I could see the flashing lights of the ambulance beyond the crowded officials and cops. It kinda felt good to know that we played a part in hopefully saving this man's life. Maybe the officials will take into consideration that some of us aren't the beasts they've believed us all to be. I could feel the hope that everyone around me felt at doing this good thing. Felix could just as easily thrown his hands up and said, "We hold him and let him die." It's what most of the guys wanted.

The gate started clattering open as soon as Felix disappeared from the guard tower's view. Those white-suited medics stood on the outside waiting for it to open wide enough to get their little bed on wheels in. The guards in the tower had their guns trained on the lobby door, waiting for one of us to make a mad dash for the opening gate to freedom. None of us moved, just watched. The gate had opened about three or four feet; the first medic had stepped through. Suddenly, Lieutenant Hernandez leaped to his feet, throwing off the blanket, and dashed naked, knocking that first medic aside and out through the open gate.

Everyone in our group was stunned. It got suddenly silent outside, and then we heard the loud cheers and laughter of those officials at the gate and the crowd beyond. We stood in place watching as the gate rattled shut and Lieutenant Hernandez was walked toward the waiting ambulance. Someone had thrown a bright red blanket over his shoulders. Cops, officials, and a couple of those women walked behind and beside him, slapping him on the back and congratulating him at how he had so effectively fooled us. He kept turning around and pointing back inside, saying something to those officials around him. It looked like he was pointing toward Cellhouse 6.

"We've gotta move the hostages!" Felix said behind gritting teeth. "That fat pig is telling them where we have the hostages! Come on, we got to move 'em *now!*" he said in a rush and turned toward the center of the prison. We all started back in with a new kind of urgency now. Felix quickly told a couple of his crew to stay in the lobby and keep an eye on the cops. A couple others were strung out at intervals in the hallway to pass the word faster if they started to come in. The rest of us made for Cellhouse 6 to tell everyone to get out of there.

By the time I got to the block, a couple of other convicts had already told everyone about the faked heart attack and how he had been pointing in this direction. The rush was on as I came in the door; weapons were grabbed, and blindfolded, naked guards were pulled out of the cells and prodded along the tier, down the stairs and out into the hallway. Felix told everyone who had a hostage to find a place and to keep no more than three hostages at any one location.

I started for the TV room to get Stanley and Weasel so we could get out of there, too. But I had to stop and watch this one guard being brought out of a cell. He wouldn't stand or walk. He kept complaining that he couldn't breathe. He said his chest hurt. He started crying and blubbering about his wife and kids. He must have heard that Lieutenant Hernandez got released for similar whining. The two convicts that brought him out of the cell glared down at him on the tier. One of them asked him, "Are you having a heart attack?" When the guard turned his head in the direction of the concerned voice, he was kicked in the face and it flipped him over on his side. The two convicts took turns kicking him and asking again and again, "How's your heart? Are you heart attacking yet?" Felix stood on the end of the tier and just watched without saying anything.

I moved on into the TV room and saw Stanley and Weasel watching the news special about the New Mexico State Prison riot. The newscaster announced the just-released hostage who had fooled the rioters into letting him go. They said that's the first hostage to get out and that he was only shaken up from the experience. I looked out the TV room windows that faced the front of the prison. There was a van with the news crew standing under the bright lights of the parking lot. I glanced back at the TV and again out the window. And shook my head at the incredibility of all this. The same crew on the TV is there making the announcement in the parking lot. What was the latest move gonna do to the negotiations that hadn't even started yet? The bitterness and anger were only reinforced by being tricked into showing compassion. The hostage getting stomped now for feinting pain was only the beginning of what was in store for him and the other hostages. So far none of the guards had been killed, but how long would that last?

Looking back into the cellblock, there were the two convicts dragging the guard hostage. Each one had hold of a foot and they were headed toward the stairwell, still taunting him about his heart.

6   Levels of Paranoia

We watched from the TV room while those last hostages were herded out. Frank was off in a cell talking with Felix and wanted us to wait on him before returning to Cellhouse 1.

Momentarily I saw Frank step from a cell on the left tier and wave at me, then plod up the tier in our direction. I stepped over to the door and he waved at me again to come on. I sauntered out on the landing, leaving Stanley and Weasel watching the blow-by-blow recap of the riot on television. Something is up; Frank had that I-got-a-deal-for-you expression on his face. I moved over to the railing that ran around the second tier and leaned against it to wait and at least listen to his next idea. He started right in with that gravelly voice, "I volunteered us to watch this terribly burnt guard. Come on, I'll show you . . ." He started back toward the cell he'd come out of. I followed saying, "Why Frank? We have enough responsibility already. We don't want to be yoked to another one." He continued leading the way and said, "We gotta keep the two worst hurt guards together. They'll be released as soon as Felix gets the negotiations started." He stopped at the cell, with his hand on the handle and said, "I've already told Felix that we'd do this. Come on brother, I need your help on this. I couldn't ask no one else," and he pulled the cell door open. Following him on in, I saw Felix first. Then the smell hit me; that sickening-sweet odor of burnt flesh and I immediately pulled my gas mask over my face. Earlier I had pulled it up to ride on top of my head while watching the TV news. I took a couple of deep breaths and moved around Felix to look at the new piece of guard meat that Frank had roped us into babysitting.

This guard laid on his back. At first glance he looked dead—eyes closed and stock still. But no, I could see he was breathing. He looked like he'd been roasted over a fire. Burnt from head to ankles, had no hair, and I could see patches of raw scalp. Huge blisters stuck out at odd angles on his face, distorting his features. I could see holes where his nose should be; but there was no nose there. There were black charred places on his arms and stomach and his legs were just raw flesh. The only places that weren't burnt were the rings around his ankles and wrists where he'd been tied.

Behind me Felix said, "You guys will have to carry him 'cuz he's been out ever since we brought him here!" I kept staring at the guard. I'd seen a few burns before, but this . . . nothing like this. I stared and said, "I'll get some help. I guess we can carry him . . ." and backed toward the door shaking my head in amazement at the hideous creature lying on the bed.

As I pulled the door open, I saw Lucky and Bear. Stepping past them I heard Lucky tell Felix, "We got big problems . . ." and I kept moving up the tier, not hearing any more.

Rushing into the TV room again, I immediately recognized the newcomers, Jeff and Frenchie. They were in an animated conversation with Stanley and Weasel. Jeff saw me and kept right on describing his grisly adventures of killing those confined on protective custody in Cellblock 4. "Brother, I cut his throat! Brother, I stabbed that rat 'til he gave up the ghost! Brother, you should of seen 'em beggin' for mercy!" Jeff was one of the most unusual persons I'd ever met, with a twisted sense of propriety that allowed him to call everyone brother. Every statement he made was started with brother or ended with brother. I'd met him a couple of years ago when we were neighbors in Cellhouse 2. I realized back then that this man was dealing with very few cards in his deck and I avoided him. And now, here he was with blood smears on his face and spatters of blood covering his clothes, telling me about his exploits in murder. As I nodded my head every so often, Jeff droned on as if we were actually having a conversation. I'd learned a long time ago that you let nuts do the talking. Glancing over at Frenchie, I saw he had a macabre grin on his face, as if he was seeing again what Jeff was describing. The clothes on him looked like they'd been soaked in blood. When Jeff finally wound down from his conquests in butchering, I said, "Man, I don't mean to interrupt you, but we got to get out of here 'cuz the cops know we're in this cellblock . . ." Jeff looked at me with surprise, then fear, and stuck out his right hand saying, "Its good seeing you brother. We'll see you later brother." I let him shake my left hand 'cuz my right hand was still full with my pipe. He dropped my hand and he and Frenchie shuffled toward the door. We watched them as they ambled down the tier talking to each other. Stanley said, "There's two wired-up, live nut cases. Aren't we lucky to have friends like that!" We kinda laughed at that but not from the humor in the statement but something else that says to laugh to cover up the chill you feel from the images left in your mind.

Shaking off the effects of those two, I explained that we had been drafted again to watch this burnt guard. Stanley looked at me as if I'd lost my mind, but he didn't say anything. I told them that I didn't like it, but what the hell—we're in for one, we might as well go for two. Moving down the tier I told them they'd better cover their noses 'cuz of the smell.

At the cell we walked right in and the only word that could describe what laid on the bed—"Wowww!" Weasel said when he saw the guard. Frank directed us to roll him on his side to get a blanket under him. Just touching his body made me cringe from the heat that radiated off him. His being unconscious made handling him a whole lot easier. Frank dropped his bag on the blanket and we all grabbed a handful of wool material. This was gonna be a lot easier and a lot lighter than the last one we'd carried. With everyone ready we lifted at once. He suddenly came alive kicking and screaming, totally startling us, and we just dropped him right back down on the bed. He kept screaming like a deranged nut, and we quickly stepped back a couple of steps to get some distance from this mad man.

Then he stopped screaming and started talking in a thoroughly pissed off voice. "Why don't you bastards just kill me and get it over with!" Everyone was already stunned from the nut roll and it completely astounded us to be cussed and challenged all in one breath. He kept talking and calling us everything from canine fornicators to chicken guano eaters. From some of the things he said, I realized I knew this guard. I startled him by asking, "Hey! Hey! Hey! What's your name?" He just looked at me not saying anything for a couple seconds. Yeah, I knew this guy. He used to work at the security gate going in and out of Prison Industries. There had been occasions when I'd had to stay at the security gate until count cleared. In prison, when it's count time, everyone has to stay where they're at until the count is made and count is cleared. Those times that I'd had to wait at the gate, I'd had conversations with this guard. He was an ex-Marine, Vietnam vet, and not too bad of a guard. I'd never known him to push his authority or look to bust anyone. "Just trying to get through an eight-hour shift," he would say.

Hesitantly, he said his name, "Donald Diego," staring at me as if he was starting to realize who I was. The look in his blood-shot eyes told me that he knew me. In his nut roll, he'd pulled his legs up and laid in a crouch on one elbow as if he was ready for the fight if we were there for that. He said, "What the hell are you doing here?" and looked around at everyone as if to say, what are you doing with these people? "We're here to help you man!" I said matter-of-factly. "We need to move you and you got my word on this, we aren't gonna hurt you." He looked back at me and just shook from anger, fear, or whatever. Frank said, "You know this guard?" I took off my gas mask and said, "Yeah, I know him! He worked at the gate at Industries." It isn't healthy in prison to get too friendly with our keepers. But I knew it would mean something to Frank so I told him. "He's a 'Nam vet!" Frank just nodded his head and looked at the guard. He had relaxed a little bit and stretched one of his burnt legs out again. I asked him, "Can you walk man?" He moved his legs and said, "I guess so . . ." and laid his other blistered leg out straight and said, "Can I have some water?" Stanley stood closest to the sink and he took a cup off the shelf, ran it full of water and handed it to me. By then the guard had sat up with his feet on the floor and immediately gulped the water down when I handed it to him. He handed the cup back, asked for more, got it and gulped that too. When he wanted more Frank said not to give him any more water just now. Watching him drink the water, I couldn't help but feel empathy for the man. He didn't deserve the hell he went through. When he handed the cup back to me I asked him, "How do ya' feel guy?" And I didn't care what anyone else thought about my concern. Sure, he was a guard, but he was a vet too, and in my book, that put him above the stigma of a screw or pig. He laid back on the bed and said, "My whole body feels stung. It doesn't hurt . . . just stung!" He raised his arm to look at it. If he could show expression on his blistered face, I'm sure it would have been disbelief in what he saw.

Felix said, "I'll get some clothes and boots for him," and he left the cell. Everyone else in the cell stood silent, staring at the guard checking himself out. He looked at the charred black places on his stomach and lightly scratched at the darkest spot then looked at his fingernail to see what came off. He said, "Can I get some more water? I'm thirsty." I looked at Frank for the go ahead and he shook his head no. I said, "Not right now. This guy is our medic," and pointed to Frank. "He was one in 'Nam too so he knows what he's doing!" The guard stared at Frank with the open veneration that all soldiers seem to look at medics with.

Felix walked in with the state clothes and a pair of old brogans and dropped them on the end of the bed. The guard pulled the pants on while laying on the bed and sat up. He stuck his bare feet in the shoes and I could see that they were too big. He pulled the laces tight and sat up. Reaching for the blue prisoner's shirt he asked, "What time is it?" I immediately said, "That's a secret and we can't tell secrets to the enemy!" He looked up at me and I grinned, or tried to, then showed him my watch.

He stomped his feet a couple times, stood up, weaved back and forth a couple times, and sat back down. I asked him, "Everything alright? We can carry you if you . . ." He leaned forward, holding his head in his hands, then puked at our feet. He groaned, wiped his mouth, and leaned back against the wall with his eyes squeezed shut.

Frank immediately said, "He drank that water too fast!" And took the cup from me and ran it full in the sink. As he handed it to the guard, he said, "Drink this slow and don't gulp it!"

After about a minute he started looking a little better, if that was possible with all the blistered burns on his face and head. We were set to go again and Felix said to blindfold him. The guard said nothing while we draped a towel over his head. Stanley ripped a strip from a sheet and tied it around his head to keep the towel in place. It was understood that we wouldn't allow the hostages to know where they were being taken. We were ready, but Felix said, "Come out on the tier for a minute," waving us all out of the cell. The guard just sat there while we filed out.

When the door shut Felix said, "There's some crazy shit going on! My people have found some good people killed! Just in the last hour they've found bodies cut to pieces! Someone or some group is catching people alone or asleep! Whoever it is, they're using an ax so get this guard to your house and watch your back!" We all stood around him soaking in the words. It put a new level to my paranoia. That radar that I felt was turned to its highest gain. It was like being in the jungle again and in a mindset that adopts to the surroundings and circumstances.

Felix moved off with Lucky and Bear who were waiting on the tier for him. We brought the guard out and he hung on to Frank's belt loop and we made our way out of the cellblock. Down the center of the hallway we moved like a military squad, feeling our way along. We knew what was in here with us. We knew and we were ready for whatever moved against us. We had a new determination to get through this madness. The way I figured, as long as we stayed awake and alert, then it didn't matter how long it took to end.

7   A Glimpse of Truth

Passing the control center, I heard movement in front of us but I couldn't see where it came from. It sounded like splashing as in someone walking and then it stopped suddenly. I adjusted my gas mask to see a little better out the eye holes, but it was no better. The smoke and darkness was too dense to make out anything. It hung like thick gauze and I didn't allow my eyes to blink for fear of something, someone hiding in it.

With Stanley on my left, I knew he'd take the brunt from whatever jumped on that side of the hallway. He held his knife like I showed him—cocked and ready. I knew Frank and the guard were right behind me. I didn't have to look, I could feel the water they splashed on the back of my legs. The guard just stumbled along. He's in bad shape and maybe we should have carried him. But we ain't got far to go. Come on, come on, just a little ways further.

I could hear Weasel back there, too; at least hanging in with me. He's such a youngster, only 20 years old, but hard as nails and I couldn't ask for a better friend at my back. It would hurt me if anything happened to him, but in a pinch, I think he would rock and roll.

When we passed the gym doors, I felt a slight breeze and the smoke cleared for a long ways down the hall. The further we moved away from the smoldering fires, the more the air seemed to clear. I could relax a little and breathe deep. Turning my head I said, "Hey Don, you still with us?" He said in an exhausted voice, "Yeah, yeah, I'm still with ya . . ."

Another helicopter passed overhead as it passed in view through the flood lights outside, I saw the familiar Red Cross on the side doors—a medevac. They're probably picking someone up.

And then we sloshed into the cellblock and Frank and I helped the guard up the steps to the second tier. "Just a little ways further, man," I said. He just grunted under the towel, sticking one wet leg in front of the other.

59

At the cell door, Stanley had it open and waiting while we half-carried the guard the last few steps. Just before we walked into the cell, I thought I spotted movement across the cell block on the other tier. Then the door closed behind me and I heard Stanley lock it. We were safe. We could relax and rest.

Boots stood by the sink and fired questions at us one after another. "Where you guys been? Man, I was worried . . . I thought you'd ran out on me . . ." Stanley made a disgusting sound and said, "You know better 'n that!" Boots went on. "I heard people go by the door but I didn't let 'em know I was in here. The relief at seeing us was obvious. He watched Frank take the towel off the guard's head, and seeing the hostage's scorched face, he said, "What happened to him?" Stanley told him, "Take a breath man. Let us get situated and we'll tell ya everything!" I could see that hurt Boots' feelings; he kinda shrunk down on the sink not saying anything else.

Frank said we should get another mattress for the new hostage. He stood in front of the guard dabbing some kind of cream on his blistered face. The guard had his eyes closed, just standing there like a patient getting ministered by his doctor.

Stanley unlocked the door and pushed it open for me. I stepped out and turned to the right. Moving hesitantly a couple of paces, I tried to see through the darkened haze in the direction where I'd seen movement. Nothing was there now, but I could swear I'd seen someone standing on the opposite tier when we came in the cellblock. I took a couple more steps and glanced into the cell door window of the cell next to ours. There was a mattress on the bed and I pulled the door open. Stepping in, I quickly moved to the bed, folded the mattress in half and stuck it under my left arm. Looking around for anything else we might need, I stepped back to the door. Nothing we could use. Just dirty clothes and trash on the cell floor. I stepped out and looked again in the direction of movement seen earlier. I took those few steps back to our cell where Stanley held the door and watched my back.

As I walked in the cell I heard Frank tell the guard, "Take a couple of these and you'll be feeling no pain!" He held out the pills and Don Diego took them one at a time, swallowing them dry.

I dropped the mattress against the wall and chuckled, "Are you pushing them drugs again, brother?" I pointed at Frank and said, "This guy here hung out at grade schools and forced little kids to take dope!" Diego tried to grin but his blistered mouth made a grimace and he quickly jerked his hand to it in a flinch of pain. He said, "It only hurts when I laugh!" and looked expectantly at the mattress on the floor. I stepped back and toed the mattress apart and told him, "Go ahead man, it's yours!" He almost fell on it to lay down.

Everyone watched him curiously for a few minutes. He laid flat on his back and looked at the ceiling. It felt odd having him in the cell with us. I'm sure everyone had questions they wanted to ask him. I had a few myself. But no one said anything. It was like an invisible barrier separated us from him. He was still a guard and our captive, but we were all captives now . . . I shook my head to shake off the weird feeling.

"Can we talk in front of him?" Stanley asked cautiously. I knew he meant the guard, Diego. I looked back at Diego and said, "We can't leave the cell every time we gotta talk." Diego looked up at me and I turned back to Stanley. "What 'cha got on your mind?" Stanley glanced around at everyone in the cell and said, "What Felix told us about those . . . those killings with the ax. Who do you think is doing that?" Frank answered, "It could be anybody. It's either a nut or a group of nuts." I spoke up with, "There's at least a dozen groups in here . . . Hell, it could be anyone." Boots said in a shaky voice, "What are you guys talking about?" I glanced at him and then back at the guard and said, "There's someone using an ax and catching people asleep or wandering around alone." I kept watching the guard, but he gave no reaction—just kept looking at the ceiling. Glancing back at Boots I said, "We ain't got nothing to worry about. The door stays locked. No one goes out alone. We're alright right here." I tried to sound as reassuring as I could, but I was as frightened as those guys were. I just couldn't let 'em see it. The silence was cloying and I waited for someone to say something else about this ax-wielding nut.

Frank turned from changing the bloody bandage on the captain's head and said, "Where's John at?" Boots said matter-of-factly, "He left hours ago. He went to find a way out!" Frank said slowly, "He did what?" Frank knew John. Hell, everybody knew him. He was a resourceful guy, one of the sneakiest guys in this joint. He worked in the electrical shop, out in Prison Industries. A few years ago he built a still inside a defunct hot water heater at the shop. For months he made just enough alcohol to entertain us on the weekends. The guards never did find it, but they sure did look for it. After one hard search, he took it apart and hid the pieces. "He's probably out there on that cold recreation yard wishing he's back in here with us," Stanley said. Everyone kinda laughed at that and it got quiet again.

We made adjustments and everyone squatted down on the floor to get comfortable. I traded places with Stanley by the door. I hunkered down into the door frame and leaned my head on my bent knees. I'd been awake since yesterday morning. My eyes felt like they were on fire. I closed them and tried to close my mind, but that was impossible . . .

Stanley said, "Where's that pot you found?" I looked up at him, remembering now that I did have some weed. "It's in my blue shirt," I said. "I left it in that flooded cell downstairs!" and immediately stood up. I'd completely forgotten about that marijuana I'd found in the investigator's office. I asked, "Who wants to go with me downstairs to get it?" Weasel lit up and said he'd go with me.

The quick trip down the stairs and retrieving the shirt I'd left on the desk was without incident. We didn't see anyone and we were back in the cell in less than five minutes.

Stanley had the cards out that he'd found in the desk of the investigator's office. He and Frank kept asking each other, "Do you know this guy?" and handing cards back and forth to each other.

We didn't have any rolling papers and settled on using the flimsy, thin paper around toilet paper rolls to twist our joints in. We rolled up six big hooters to smoke and passed one out to everyone in the cell. I asked our hostage if he smoked pot and he said, "Occasionally." So he got one too.

With everyone lit up, the small confines of the cell filled with the pungent smoke. I took a lung full, held it for a few seconds, blew it out and drew in another, waiting for that familiar euphoria that for some reason wouldn't come. Maybe I was expecting too much too fast, and continued puffing on the joint. It tasted pretty good.

I watched the guard propped up on one elbow, smoking his joint like he knew what he was doing. This guy was alright. Here he was, our hostage, smoking a joint with us as if we were having a party. I wondered what he would say to this episode when this madness was all over.

Frank interrupted my bending thoughts with, "Check this one out. Do you know this guy?" I took the card he pushed at me and focused my eyes on the mug shot photo in the top corner. Looking back at Frank I said, "Yeah, I know this maggot. He's a rat!" Frank said, "Read what it says!" I took another puff on my joint and squinted through the trailing smoke and started reading the typed print on the card. "Subject refuses to cooperate with investigation. It is recommended that subject be made to appear to cooperate. Subject has vital information concerning Case #447 investigation conducted by Deputy Warden Florez. Subject placed on Protective Custody 6-18-79. Subject denies knowledge of investigation. Recommend subject be questioned again in 90 days." I blew out the smoke and asked, "What the hell is this?" Frank held the other cards up saying, "All these say the similar thing!" I reread the card I held. The joint in my other hand forgotten. Looking at the picture on the card again, I remembered the incident which caused this guy to have to go to Protective Custody. A note was found in a captain's shirt pocket that was sent to the prison laundry. (Guards and staff at the prison used the free laundry.) This note that was found by a convict laundry worker said, "I have information about who's selling drugs if you'll let me out of lock up." The laundry worker who found the note brought it to the cellblock for everyone to read. It had happened before that information was gleaned from the pockets of our keepers. When the writer of that note was released from the hole, he was moved into the same cellblock. Everyone knew him or thought they did. I remember standing out on the tier, leaning against the railing, when he carried his box of personal things into the cellblock. After he got moved into a cell, the guards left and a couple of us went to him. We showed him the note that he denied writing. But his guilt was already decided. He was beaten, stabbed, and left for dead at the front gate to the cellblock. He was rushed to the hospital. They saved his life and when he was well enough, placed in the Cellblock 4 (Protective Custody). And that's where he had to stay if he wanted to live.

Glancing back at Frank I said, "Let me see some of those others." He had a glum scowl twisted across his face and said, "Read this one!" I took the offered card and immediately recognized the photo on it. Charlie Knolles, everyone knew him too. A couple of years ago he had gotten into an extremely serious hassle because of a rumor that said he was an informer. No one bothered to check it out or find out the truth. In a matter of days, his name was linked to the discovery of a bag full of weapons, drugs, keys and a box of .38 bullets. No one could understand how he would have known where the bag was hidden, but it made no difference at the time.

Word came from the Mexican group that owned the bag that Charlie had to stop breathing. It was expected that the whites were to take care of him. One night he was jumped, stabbed, and thrown down in the stairwell. Somehow he lived through it. He lost an eye and his back was broken. He too lived on Protective Custody 'cuz it was the only place he could live. I remember him 'cuz he was a pretty good tattoo artist and he had a life sentence. I looked at the typed words written on his card. "Individual pointed out by informant to have possible knowledge of contraband found. To preserve informant's identity, individual to be identified as informer to Case #123 investigation. Individual placed on Protective Custody 3-7-78."

I looked up from reading this card with shock, anger and Frank watching me. "They set him up!" he said. I couldn't speak at first. I looked at the name on the bottom of the card. It's the deputy warden's signature across from the space provided for approval. I glanced back at Frank and said, "They did this deliberately. They set him up to look like he told about that bag. They did it to protect the rat so he could keep ratting, they . . . they . . . they . . ." My mouth got kinda tangled up with the words I wanted to say and feelings that fired through my mind. Our keepers have been pitting us against each other for their own purposes. They'd push a button and know how we'd react. They know the stigma of having a rat label on a man in here. It especially rankled me because I believed Charlie had ratted on that bag. He had tried to talk to me about it, but I turned my back and wouldn't listen. And now knowing the truth, it especially hurt 'cuz we were friends. He even put a tattoo on me.

It was a sobering moment. The pot was forgotten. I threw my joint on the floor. I didn't want to be high—I wanted to find out more of what was on those cards.

Everyone in the cell was reading them, passing them around for all to see. Some of the cards had two and three cards stapled together. Some had "Reliable Informant" written across the top. Some had dates that were recent and some were five to eight years old. The ones that had "Reliable Informant" on them had informed about drugs, weapons, escape plans, fights, and killings. Some of these rats have been telling things for years.

We read each card over and over and found six that we believed were intentionally set up by captains, the deputy warden, and other ranking guards. These six were of incidents that one of us in the cell could remember. There were others with older dates on them that we didn't recognize and maybe Felix or some old timers would remember. No one ever guessed or suspected that this had been going on. The guards and officials that approved this were of that little select group that all convicts knew not to get crossed up with. It was known that they would make your time miserable if, for whatever reason, you got sideways with one of them. Nothing was ever on paper about this group of keepers, but we knew. And now we had proof of their tactics. We had the proof to make changes, but first we had to get it out of the joint.

Frank counted them and there were 34 cards total. Twenty-six were assigned to Protective Custody, eight were assigned to general population. There's no telling where these eight informers were, but we knew where to find 26, and six of those were set up to look like informers. Frank said, "We've gotta find Felix, give him these cards and he'll get 'em to the media in the negotiations." He fanned the cards out saying, "He'll know about some of those others with older dates."

It had started to get dark outside. It was pitch-dark in the cellblock. The only sounds we heard the last couple of hours were the overflights of the National Guard Helicopters. It was decided that Boots and Weasel would stay with the hostages. As Frank, Stanley, and I made ready to leave, I told them about the movement I'd seen earlier. "Maybe they have hostages in a cell and they might know where we can find

Felix," I said. We left the cell and stood out on the tier for a moment and I pointed across the cellblock to where I thought I'd seen someone. We headed out around the walkway from cell to cell to find one occupied. In the general location where I'd seen something earlier, we heard talking in the cell. They had their cell door window covered and so Frank knocked on the door. It suddenly got quiet in the cell and he knocked again. An angry voice on the inside said, "What the fuck ya want?" Frank said in his gravel voice, "I gotta find Felix." We heard whispering and the snap of the lock on the door being turned. As the door came open, we stepped back a step. Two convicts stood in the doorway with knives in their hands and one said, "What'cha want him for?" Frank held up the file cards and said, "We found some good information in these that'll help us all in the negotiation." The two guys moved forward and we backed up. I didn't know what they had in mind and slowly raised my lead pipe and lightly bounced it on my shoulder. Stanley stood on the other side of Frank but he hadn't touched his knives in his belt. When the two guys cleared the doorway, another convict stepped out behind them and he said, "I know you!" He indicated Frank and said, "I don't know where Felix is at, but we can find out . . ." He held a two-way radio and put it up to his mouth and said into it, "Come in Chopper One! Chopper One come in!" Then he said to Frank, "You guys want to know what's going on? You gotta find one of these walkie-talkies." Frank said, "Yeah, we'll have to get us one." A couple seconds later I recognized Felix's voice. "This is Chopper One, what's up?" The guy with the radio spoke into it. "The medic found something for you." Felix said, "I'm busy right now. Can it wait?" Frank shook his head and said, "Find out where he's at . . ." The guy said into his radio, "It can't wait. Wants to bring it to you." Felix came right back with, "I'm in the German area." And that's all he said. Then the guy with the radio said, "You guys didn't go to the meeting. If you did, you'd know." He pulled a folded piece of paper out of his pants pocket, stepped back into the light of the cell, and said, "You need one of these directories too." And he studied the paper for a couple seconds. "The German area is the kitchen!" And sarcastically he said, "You know where that is, don't 'cha . . .? He chuckled and his two friends grinned like shit eaters that they probably were. They stepped back into the cell and as we walked by, I heard the lock snap.

Moving down the tier, I realized we needed a radio. I had a new respect for Felix and the riot leaders. They had devised a code for the locations inside the joint so we could use the radio. When we reached the stairwell I told Stanley, "We gotta find us a radio and one of those coded directories." We continued on down the stairway and into the gathering darkness.

8   Discovering What Death Is

At the bottom of the stairs, Frank moved out from between us and took the lead. He acted as if he was oblivious to the darkness that swallowed him at the corridor door. We could hear him lumbering away and I hissed at Stanley, "Come on!" and broke into a dog trot. Any semblance of stealth is lost on the racket we made catching Frank. We caught him at the chow hall doors and I had to ask, "What the hell is the rush?" I could hear him puffing air next to me but he didn't say anything, just kept striding ahead.

Moving through the huge dining room he slowed his pace after plowing into a table that was bolted to the floor. It was like playing blind-man's-bluff in a pinball machine. We bounced off four or five tables before we found the aisle between them.

We made it to the front and crept around the steel serving line, more concerned about stumbling into something lying in our path than who might be lying in wait. It was like an obstacle course through a metal junk yard. Pieces of the serving line lay scattered all the way to the kitchen door.

It was a swinging door and we pushed on through it and got blinded by a half dozen flashlight beams. My first instinct was to throw my hands up and duck out of the way. Then I heard Felix's voice say, "It's okay!" and in a louder voice he said, "Was that you guys making all that noise?" Squinting in the direction of his voice, "We couldn't see worth a shit!" I snarled.

Off to the left, further back in the kitchen, I saw other lights moving and someone said, "There's no one back here!" and Frank quickly rushed over to Felix with the cards. Others with flashlights kept moving around the kitchen interior as if they were looking for something or someone.

Wading over, I heard Felix say, "Yeah, we can get these to the media. But we *need* to get 'em to the Governor." He held a flashlight pointed down at the cards he had. Moving closer, I noticed the water at his feet had a pinkish tint to it. I stepped on past Felix and Frank. They were discussing strategy about the use of information on the cards. I moved next to a steel table looking at the floor. From the glare of the flashlights moving around I could see fairly well and the water turned from pink to red. Then I saw the shape of a body laying on its back. Further down I could see another one. They both lay in the water between two food prep tables. One of the guys with a flashlight waded by on the opposite side of the table on my left. As he passed, his light flashed over the first body and it looked familiar. I turned and said, "Hey, point your light over here!" He did.

As soon as the light hit the face, I knew who it was. It was John. "Aah fuck!" I moaned and just stared at my gutted friend. He didn't make it out . . . He didn't make it . . . Then I heard Stanley moving toward me saying, "Who is it man?" He rushed over and brushed by me to stand over John's body, glaring down with clenched fists. I couldn't move but I couldn't look away either. Two other flashlights moved up and I could hear whispered voices say, "Who is it? It's their partner . . ." His chest and stomach were cut open. His guts were floating in the bloody water around his body. I took a couple steps closer and Stanley kneeled down in the water beside him. We both knew John, but he and Stanley were long-time friends before I got to Santa Fe. Stanley reached his hand out, touching John's shoulder, then his face, and glared at me with a stare that slugged me and sobbed, "He's DEAD!!" He couldn't speak identifiable words, just syllables that kinda crooned out in an anguished whimper.

Felix's voice at my right shoulder said, "We heard him screaming when we were out in the hallway . . . When we got here, he was standing there trying to hold his guts out of the water." His hand came up pointing. "Look at the other one. He's been chopped in the head. It was that nut with the ax. We think we know who it is," he said. I couldn't take my eyes off John. And Stanley touched him again and said in a bewildered voice, "He's still warm!"

I turned my head, looking at Felix's face, and said, "Who do you think it is that did this?" I looked around the darkened kitchen knowing they had already searched it but wanting, hoping for a chance at whoever did this to John. I want revenge. Then Felix said, "We think it's a nigger—one of my crew saw him about an hour ago!" The announcement is startling—no, not a black. A black wouldn't do this. The mind-set just didn't fit. "Are you sure?" I asked. He nodded his head in affirmation but I still couldn't fathom it being a black dude.

Then Stanley got my attention saying, "Let's get him off the floor," and he stood up. I moved to John's feet, bent down, and got a grip on his ankles. Stanley had a hold under his shoulders and we lifted as one and laid John's body on top of the stainless steel prep table. With our hands we silently picked his still-steaming guts out of the water and placed them in a spreading pile between his legs.

We both stood at the table looking at John's body. I remember meeting him three years ago when I first got out of the fish tank, i.e., the receiving unit at the prison. He was one of the first to enlighten me on what to expect, the do's and don'ts of this New Mexican mad house. He was a little squirelly, but he was a friend and in there, friendships were rare. And it twisted my heart to see him like that.

Then Frank's gravel voice across the table said, "Come on, we're going to Cellblock 4 (Protective Custody) to find those six guys on the cards." Felix and his crew were already filing out of the kitchen through the guard's chow hall. We just turned and sloshed away from the body toward the lights.

At the door three of the crew waved us on out and they fell in behind us. We were a line of nine wading like a troop of 20. I barely heard Stanley say behind me, "We gotta find the mother fucker who done that to him!" I silently nodded my head in agreement and kept following the flashlights in front of me.

We passed a couple of the bodies I'd seen earlier by the control center. Further on we passed psych. services. It still smoked and steamed. Someone ahead said that the old men upstairs had gotten out. They broke out one of the dorm windows. A few had died in the fire but most were hurt jumping to the ground from the second floor window.

We kept going past Cellhouse 6. It was deserted and I am sure that was 'cuz Lt. Hernandez ran his mouth. Everyone thought Cellhouse 6 would be the first place the forces outside would retake. If they pumped their nuts up to come in, they'd be surprised in there.

Just past Cellhouse 6 I noticed the water getting shallow with each step and a few paces further, we were on dry flooring. A welcoming, pleasant change and then we reached the solid steel door at the entrance of Cellblock 4.

Felix pulled on the handle and the door swung back silently. He and Frank walked in first and the rest of us tramped in behind and stopped, staring around in the shadowy darkness.

We were in a reception-guard post area. A couple of desks sat against the wall in front of us. Over the desks, tacked to the wall, were two large roster boards with cell numbers and their names on them. Felix and Frank were eyeing the roster board, looking for cell locations and scribbling on the cards. Off to the right were those opaque windows. It was bright on that side 'cuz lights from the outside perimeter blazed in on the cellblock.

I'd never been in that cellblock. It was built different from the others. Its cells are set back to back from each other with the tiers running outside next to the walls of the structure. The reception area where we stood is actually the second floor/tier of the four floors in the cellblock with the first tier in the basement. It's quiet as a tomb. The only sound is our whispering to each other.

Felix told two of his crew to stay at the door and we looked around at the rest of us and said, "Let's check this side first," and he and Frank led the way around to the left, the dark side. The gates stood open and we filed onto the walkway at a pretty good pace. Felix wanted to get this search over with and we all knew what was in there . . . at least we thought we knew.

Moving past the first cell, I glanced through the bars and didn't see anyone in the cell—just a bed, sink, and toilet—and the sliding cell door stood open. As we passed the second cell, I thought I saw a body crouched down by the back cell wall, but I couldn't be sure and Felix kept moving on down the tier. After two or three more cells that had unrecognizable shapes inside, I quit looking. All the cells were open that we passed and they were darkened and I couldn't really see anything inside.

Then Felix stopped and shined his light inside the cell. I moved up and around the guy in front of me. When I looked in the cell, I had to shake my head. The cell occupant laid on his stomach with a wire around his neck, his legs were pulled up with the wire stretched and wrapped around his ankles. He's kinda bowed backwards. His head hung forward and it looked broken. He laid in a puddle of blood and little streams of it ran to the cell door and puddled all across the cell front. His arms were splayed out in front, as if he was holding himself up. And there was just a bloody stub where his left hand should have been.

Frank and Felix gingerly stepped around the blood and entered the cell. Felix said, "The hair looks the same color!" He looked at the mug shot on the card and back at the body. Frank said, "We gotta be sure . . ." and he pulled sideways on the taunt wire between the neck and ankles, tipping the body over. Felix had his light pointed at the face and said, "It's him!"

They moved out of the cell and continued down the walkway for the next one. I kept looking at the floor so as not to step in anything or trip on the trash that lay scattered. Up ahead I saw a rope hanging from the tier above and leaning out over the railing, my gaze followed the rope down. The guy behind me pointed his light and at the end of the rope hung a naked, fat body. It hung about a foot off the bottom floor, like a chandelier. "That's a child molester," the guy behind me muttered. I looked again as I passed the rope and his neck looked like it had been stretched a lot further than it should have been. Someone further back said, "That's the one they slid down the rope and jumped up and down on his shoulders to stretch that neck a little!" Someone laughed and said, "Yeah, he's that one that bragged about what he did to those kids!" I vaguely remembered something about a pervert who had been found out by him bragging to others.

Frank and Felix had stopped ahead and were already comparing the card with the body in the cell. I stepped closer and could see the cell door was locked. It look like pieces of a cloth had been tied on the bars to prevent the cell door from opening. Looking closer, the cell door was jammed sideways off the track but, the bottom four bars on the door had been cut out. It looked like the occupant had tried to prevent anyone from getting in to him. It didn't stop them 'cuz there a body laid tied to his bunk. He had long, deep burns up and down his chest and stomach. Only a cutting torch can make burns like that. The lights flashing in and around the cell made it clear that he had died in much pain. He still had the last scream twisted across his face. They moved on again in a rush.

On ahead Felix and Frank rounded the corner onto the lighted side of the cellblock. When I made the corner, they were all stopped and I heard Frank say, "What the hell . . ." I moved up behind them to see what the problem was and all across the tier there was a pile of smoking bodies. One of the guys with us started retching and I was glad I had a gas mask on. We stood staring at the pile of six, eight, ten, twelve . . . bodies. I couldn't really count them because they were all kinda jumbled together and in places they looked melted together. Empty bottles of dry-cleaning fluid lay at our feet. Someone had stacked them up and tried to burn them. They were stacked so deep that we couldn't get around without stepping on them.

So, we backtracked around the walkway between the two sides of the cellblock. I stayed behind Frank and asked him, "How many more we gotta find?" Felix in front said, "We got one more on the tier with that stack of bodies, two more on the third tier and one in the basement. We kept moving around and down the tier past the child molester and to the reception area at the entrance. There the guy behind me gave his flashlight to me and said, "I don't need to see any more . . . I'll wait here!" He had puked on his shirt and I couldn't really blame him for not wanting to look at any more. I took the light and followed at the back end of the line. And I'm not sure I wanted to see any more either.

There really wasn't any need for flashlights on this right side because the outside perimeter lights kept this side of the cellblock lit up. Moving along from cell to cell, they were empty. No one inside. When I caught up to Frank, Felix, and the rest of them, they were gathered at the door of an empty cell. I could see a pair of crutches laying on the cell floor and Frank said, "This is where Charlie Knolles lives . . ." I looked back in the cell but Charlie wasn't there. I glanced down at the tier at the pile of bodies on the far end. Felix passed me going toward the front again. Stanley walked by and Frank said, "Come one, we've got a few more to find and we can get out of here!" I just looked at him not knowing what to say. I guess I was hoping we'd find Charlie, find him alive. I plodded in line behind Frank just looking at his back and moving down the empty tier.

At the entrance again, Felix had already started up the steel steps to the third tier. He said, "The two up here are on the same side!" And everyone mounted the steps behind him. At the top he went around the tier on the left—the dark side.

The many things I'd witnessed in my life up to now had been a fairly good buffer for what I'd seen so far. I'd been in war and seen torn, burnt, dead bodies before. The calluses that were on my mind at an early age allowed me to look on tragedy without a blink. But nothing in my wildest nightmares could have compared to or prepared me for what waited around the dark side of the third tier.

Those first few cells we passed were open and empty. Pointing my light into each cell, they looked like they all were empty. About halfway down the walkway, we found the first body, and the other bodies—and the blood.

They were tied to the outside of the cell bars, one after the other. Each one had been butchered with methodical engineering. There were at least 10 bodies lined down the tier. Each one filleted. They had to have been tied to the bars first. The flesh on the legs had been cut to the bone and down the length of the bone and left hanging at the knee. The same had been done to the arms, face, chest—cut and left hanging in bloody strips. In front of me, Frank said, "These guys were probably brought out one at a time, tied, cut, and left to bleed out!" I kept swallowing as we slowly passed one and the next and the next. We couldn't help but step in the half-coagulated rivers of blood on the tier.

We passed them all and my mind was screaming at me to get out, get away. I wanted to lift my gas mask and spit 'cuz I could taste something from my stomach. But I didn't care to take my mask off. I knew I'd smell what I was seeing, so I kept swallowing.

Felix stopped ahead and said, "This one's empty!" and he moved on for two more cells and stopped again. Then he started back toward me saying, "These two guys are probably hanging on the bars back there." He held two cards in his right hand. "There's no way we can identify any of those on these cards!" And he started to pass me, to go back past the hung, butchered bodies. I had to say something. "How many more do we gotta find? We ain't gonna find any of these guys alive! Why are we doing this? Let's get the hell out!" He looked at me kinda strange and said, "We got one more in the basement and then we're out of here!" He started to move on and I said, let's go around the other side . . ." and three or four others behind me agreed. Felix turned around and we followed him to the end of the tier. No one wanted to walk past that bloody mess again.

We made it to the lighted side and that near-panic feeling subsided in my mind. I couldn't help but look in cells as we passed them. One guy sat dead on the commode with a pipe driven through his mouth and it stuck out the back of his head. Each cell had someone in it and each had been killed in an equally grotesque manner. And these guys were alive just yesterday. It was like a horror movie, that was live, in bright, vivid colors.

Then we were at the stairs again and Felix told the three at the front door that we'd be a minute going to the basement. We passed them and went on down to the first tier and the old death row. Death row had been closed in name only. Now it was part of Protective Custody and still a dark, dingy place.

We found all the cells locked closed. The lock box that controls the cell doors was open. But from the looks of it, someone had jammed the levers that open the doors. They probably tried to open too many cells at once and broke the cables. Empty dry-cleaning fluid bottles lay everywhere at our feet. There had to have been 15 to 20 empty bottles scattered around. All the cells had been doused with the stuff. One of the guys with us said he still smelled dry-cleaning fluid. The whole row of eight cells had been burned with all occupants still inside. We couldn't identify anything as people inside the cell. Just piles of blackened, burnt mass. Some of the cells still smoked. The soot from the smoke hung from the bars and ceiling like black ribbons floating in a breeze.

Frank counted down the cells to get the right cell location from the card. The fire had burned off the numbers outside the cell. The contents of the cell that he said was the right one didn't resemble a man. I don't know what that was on the floor, but it sure didn't look human. Felix said, "We've confirmed that the pictures on the cards match two guys. We can still use the cards in the negotiations." He looked puzzled about saying that and then he said, "No, no, we won't tell the negotiators about these cards." He held them up. "We'll demand that we see the Governor and give them to him!" Then he turned and headed toward the stairs.

We fell in behind and passed two open doors that led deeper into the basement. Above one door a sign read, "Death Chamber," and I hesitated and said, "We were in that room with the gas chamber this morning and we saw some guys trying to use it. Maybe one of those on the cards is in there. Let's go check it out!"

We moved through the doorway under the sign and I could hear our hollow steps walking down a long hallway. We passed some empty waiting cells, a room with chairs and tables inside, and through a huge concrete portal and there it sat.

Our flashlight beams cut a path to the dull, gray-green globe that squatted in the middle of the floor. The big steel chamber door stood open.

There were no green and red flashing lights on the panel. It lay on the floor, broken in pieces with wires hanging out. I kept moving my light around where the steel cabinets were. They were all busted open. The guys hadn't found the cyanide or acid.

But the five bodies inside the chamber were just as dead. Four of them looked like they were stabbed to death. One strapped to the chair had been strangled. He still had the pieces of wire twisted around his neck. Frank announced that none of them matched the pictures.

I guess I had to know what happened here. Looking at these bodies, I don't know if I was disappointed that those guys didn't find the elements to make this piece of state justice work. In the end, those dead in the chamber died the old-fashioned way—individually and by hand.

I moved away from the chamber, shaking my head. I'd seen so much death that I'd never found it fascinating or shocking. What are the officials and guards going to do when they get back inside this madhouse? They caused all this—they caused it with their sadistic games for power. We were locked up and treated like animals, prodded with the brute force of state justice. Then when a magical period of time had passed, we would be set free and expected to act normally. The state locks people up and forces them to live in conditions that are already known to cause this kind of madness to eventually happen. When is society going to learn that they can't allow this to happen? The thoughts kept racing in my mind, the images of what I'd seen seared painfully on the back of my eyes and I felt sick.

9 Fear of Sleep

Watching the others in our search party move around the chamber, they looked as awed as I was at first seeing this thing—the ultimate machine for the state's revenge. The curiosity was centered on the chamber and not the dead within. They had already been determined to be of no interest. All attention was on the gadget of death.

Stanley meandered by and stopped, said something about the laundry, and wandered over to the door that led down the ramp into the lower basement. That was the same door we had come through hours earlier when we had heard noises in this room. Watching him, he just stood there holding the door open, looking at something beyond. Maybe we could get back to the hallway in that direction. I moved over beside him.

A few ceiling lights still threw out a feeble glow from further down. The light shined yellow off the muddy water that nearly filled that lower part of the basement. It looked like it came about halfway up the ramp, probably four-and-a-half, five-feet deep. There was no way I was even going to attempt to wade through it. I stepped back and mumbled through my mask, "Let's get the hell out of here!" He nodded his head and pushed the door shut.

Together we marched across the floor past the chamber and toward Frank. He looked as if he'd seen enough and was ready to move out. Felix saw us walking through the portal and I heard him shout to his crew, "Let's go, let's go!!" and they caught us at the stairs going up.

With Frank on point, we climbed out of the basement and on out into the hallway. No one said anything until we reached the control center. There Stanley said, "I want to find a radio so we'll know what's going on." Giving my flashlight to him, he crawled through the broken glass into the control center. Frank and others in Felix's crew shined their lights inside to help him locate the radio. Felix said, "Get one of those radio chargers too," pointing his light at one on the floor. Felix handed me a slip of paper saying, "This has got all the locations on it. Try not to say anything too clear. I'll call for the medic," and he pointed at Frank, "and don't pay any attention to the bullshit you'll hear on it." Frank came right back with, "You're Chopper One, right?" And Felix said, "Me and my crew is, but there's others using the radio so be cool on what you say." Stanley leaped out through the control window with a radio and charger and we were set to go.

Felix and his crew waded off through the gates and toward the front of the joint. We three—Stanley, Frank, and myself—moved down the hallway toward our acquired hovel. Considering the circumstances, we now had two flashlights, a radio with a battery charger, and a better idea of what was going on. The darkness around us and the next few hours ahead of us didn't seem as desolate. We thought the worst was behind us.

The sounds of us wading in the ankle-deep water were the only sounds we heard. For as far as our flashlight beams could penetrate, we were the only ones in the long corridor. Wisps of smoke blew by in both directions like kites broken loose from their strings.

Reaching the cell, I lifted my gas mask so Weasel could recognize us when he peeked past the curtain. When he pushed the door open, he stood there with a big "welcome home" grin on his face. He and Boots wasted no time in asking one question after another.

Stanley plugged into the radio charger, stuck the radio in the socket and turned it on. We listened for a few minutes at the babbles of threats and challenges coming from others that had radios. Turning it down to a whisper, Stanley told Boots to sit near it and listen for anything of importance. He kept one ear cocked on the radio speaker and the other one listening to what the rest of us were saying.

Frank checked on the Captain. His face was swollen to a point that it looked like a mask on a mask. One eye had swelled completely shut, and the other to just a slit. He still didn't blink or move. The soft susurration of his breath was the only indication of life.

The burnt guard Diego sat on his mattress and watched us and listened at the conversation around him. He had a cup of water in his hand and every time he moved his arm to take a sip, he'd wince from the pain in the movement.

We briefly described not being able to find anyone alive on those cards during our trip to Cellblock 4. Stanley mentioned finding John in the kitchen and the conversation suddenly got quiet.

When we entered the cell, I stayed by the door. After locking it, I leaned against the door frame. With the door locked I felt a little better, but I wanted to stay near it to make sure it stayed locked. Sliding down into a crouch in the door frame, I tried to relax. Resting my head on my folded knees, I listened to the murmur of indistinct voices on the radio. My whole body throbbed with strain. My legs were sopping wet, my right leg twitched and ached from walking on this torn shoe sole. My right shoulder burned from lugging the pipe that I'd taped to my right hand. I shut my eyes just to rest them a little while. Frank droned on about something to do with the negotiations.

The next thing I was aware of, the door was open and someone was standing over me. At the same time, I lunged up to my feet and slammed my shoulder in his chest and drove him across the width of the tier into the railing, hopped back and brought my pipe to knock his head off. By that moment I was fully awake and the face I was focusing on, to blast into another world, wasn't the enemy. It was Shaggy—a friend. He was staring at me as if I'd lost my mind, with a mixed expression of fear and surprise. Lowering my arm I said, "Where'd you come from Shaggy?" He rubbed his chest and said, "You hurt my frooont . . ." he was either high or drunk, probably high on drugs.

Frank came out of the cell behind me and said, "What are you doing Shaggy?" A half grin moved across Shaggy's face and he said, "I'm,-I'm-I'm lookin' forrr someone . . ." It was obvious that he was flying on something. I looked up and down the darkened cellblock and said, "Come on in the cell. You can stay with us," and I stepped to the side so he could get in the door. He stumbled forward saying, "Whooo's in there . . .?" and Frank said, while looking at me with a puzzled expression on his face, "You know everyone in there Shaggy." Shaggy took three or four faltering steps into our cell and stopped. Frank and I started to follow him in when he spun around saying, "He ain't innn here . . ." and stepped to the door. I moved in front of him to block his path and said, "Man, why don't you stay here with us." "No!!" He spit the word in my face before I could finish. Frank quickly said, "Who are you looking for? Maybe we know where he's at." Shaggy stared at me as if he wanted to bite me. He said, "Let me out!" I stepped back and he staggered past me out the door. I moved out on the tier behind him and he shuffled on down the walk while I stood by the open door. I said to his back, "Shaggy, why don't you come back and wait with us?" He didn't respond and kept walking away to disappear in the surrounding darkness of the cellblock. Frank stepped out beside me and looked in the direction that we could hear Shaggy's receding stumbling steps. Frank looked at me and said, "We couldn't make him stay!" I shook my head and said, "Maybe we should have." We both moved back in the cell and I pulled the door shut.

After locking it this time, I bumped it with my shoulder to make sure it stayed locked. Stanley laughed and said, "We were all asleep. I woke up to see you push him out." I looked at him and said, "I was just lucky that it was Shaggy," and I moved over to the sink.

Splashing cold water on my face, more cobwebs loosened in my mind and I knew I'd not get that lucky again. I couldn't let myself get too comfortable. I was still bone tired, but I couldn't allow myself to sleep. I took a couple of the Captain's stay-awake pills out of my pocket. My hands shook as I looked at the pills for a moment. Then I threw them in my mouth and reached for the cup to run some water in it.

After drinking the water, I stepped back to the door and leaned on it, listening to the ramblings of tired and frightened men around me. Boots said something about going out and finding Shaggy and making him come back. That idea was discussed and forgotten. I didn't care what was said as long as the door stayed locked. It was our first line of defense and safety.

Stanley turned the volume up on the radio and everyone quieted to listen to the exchange from an official outside and someone on the inside. Someone was trying to gain permission to bring a badly hurt convict from the lobby to the front gate.

My watch said it was 1:00 in the morning and I tried to imagine what was going on out in the dorms and cellblocks. I shook off the thoughts of some nut creeping around the joint with an ax. The flash image of John laying in the bloody water fled through my mind. Then Omar with his last bloody breath popping bubbles at his throat. I squeezed my eyes with my thumb and forefinger, trying to push the faces of my dead friends away. Such a waste, such a waste.

When I looked up, the burnt guard, Diego asked, "Can I use the bathroom?" I told him, "Sure, come on!" The cell only had a sink in it. The commodes and showers were at the far end of the tier. Frank helped the guard up to his feet and I unlocked the door. I didn't bother to blindfold him. He already knew we were in Cellhouse 1. I had Stanley hand me one of the flashlights off the desk but I didn't turn it on.

Stepping out of the cell, the guard followed and together we ambled down the tier. I still hadn't repaired the tape on my right boot and it made a kind of slapping noise. We moved around the end of the tier and to the other side of the cellblock. There at the restroom door I blinked the flashlight on and off to see what was inside. I stayed by the door as he went in and relieved himself in the direction of a dozen piles of smashed and broken porcelain commodes.

I watched the stairway and entrance to the cellblock below me. When I glanced down the tier, I could barely make out the darker shape of someone standing on the opposite tier by our cell. The shape moved and I knew it to be Stanley. Yeah, he's over there watching my back.

When the guard finished, he came out and whispered, "That's the first time I've pissed on the floor!" I chuckled at this point of humor and we moved back toward the cell.

Everyone was wide awake and drinking lukewarm coffee when we made it back into the cell. I asked Frank for his gray duct tape and repaired my waterlogged boot again. Stanley found some dry socks and I had to have a pair of those as well. It's amazing how dry, warm feet can make a person feel better.

The discussion started about making a run for more food and cigarettes. Weasel wanted to make a trip to Dorm B-1 for the things in his locker. It was decided that they would all go and that I would stay with the hostages.

They'd be alright as long as they watched what they were doing. I knew Frank and Stanley could handle themselves in the heat of battle, but I wasn't so sure about Boots and Weasel. As they prepared themselves to leave, I gave Boots one of my knives and told him, "Don't lose this or let anyone take it from you!" He assured me that he'd bring it back and then I slapped him a couple of times on the shoulder, nodding my head. I hadn't known him very well before this shit all started but I felt a kindred liking for him and I didn't want to see him hurt.

Weasel stood by the door waiting for the go-ahead to unlock it and lead the way. He was anxious to do something, anything. I moved over to him smiling. He was a good person, more courage than sense sometimes. I knew him in the county jail before we were sent to this madhouse. He was only 21 years old and it was his first time in prison, so he was still naive. I'd given him his nickname "Weasel" because he had that pointed face with wisps of hair on his chin that he called his "beard."

Over the months and years, the name stuck. Standing in front of him I started peeling off the tape from my hand and wrist. When I had the pipe detached from my arm, I handed it over to him and said, "Be careful out there. Stay close to these guys and don't let anyone that you don't know get inside the length of this pipe!" I helped him retape it to his right hand and he was ready.

Glancing around the room at them all, it felt like I was sending friends off to war. As each one passed going out the door, I told them to be careful and stay together. Then they were gone and I pulled the door shut, locked it, and shouldered it a few times to be sure.

Moving over to the foot of the bed, I sat down and looked at the one open eye of the Captain. No change there, just the same blank stare. I glanced at Diego as he started to say something. The radio squawked and squawked again. Then a voice asked to bring out another badly hurt convict to the front gate. We both listened as permission was given to come out of the lobby. The radio went silent after that.

Glancing back at the burnt guard, he looked at me inquisitively and said, "What's gonna happen to me and the Captain? I know you know what the plan is . . ." He gave me more credit than I deserved but I had to say something. "As soon as the negotiations reach an agreement, you'll both be released." I looked at the Captain. "He'll be released as soon as it gets daylight. At least that's the plan," I said. I tried to change to subject then because I didn't know what was gonna happen. "How are you feeling. Is there much pain?" Knowing that if I was burned like he was, I'd be screaming. He said, "It's starting to hurt more but I'm trying to stay still and not move." I dug a couple of red pills out of my shirt and handed them to him. As he swallowed them and sipped water from the cup he held I asked, "Where were you at when all this started?" I sat forward and listened. He said, "I was with the Captain when he and the Lieutenant went into E-2 dorm to make count." He looked as if he was in pain remembering, so I changed the subject again. "Where do you live at? Where are your folks? You don't live around here, do you?" He looked at his bandaged hand and said, "Yes, I'm from Santa Fe. All my people live around here." I could only read the expression in his eyes and the tone of his voice. He sounded miserable and abandoned in talking about his wife and young daughter as if he didn't expect to see them again. He took a sip of water and said, "My mother is real old and I know she's worried sick about me. I hope she's okay." Then he sat quietly looking at the cup in his hands. Neither one of us said anything for a few minutes. I wondered for the first time about my family. What would my mother be thinking? My wife? . . .

Shaking off those thoughts, I got up and moved over to the sink. As I was running water into a cup, Diego said, "What are you gonna do when this is all over?" I drank the cup full of water and looking back at him I said, "I ain't thought about afterwards, shit . . . I'm too busy trying to get through the here and now!" I felt annoyed at the questions. When this was all over, he would be going to a hospital and I would be very fortunate if I didn't get my head stomped. Running the cup full again, I drank it and said, "There's a nut out there," I pointed toward the door, "and he's got an ax, killing people. That's my main concern right now. That and all the piggies out front who might run in here any minute." He had heard us talking about the nut with the ax. He asked again, "What's gonna happen with me? You gonna let me go?" I tried to soften my words and I tried to sound reassuring and said, "You'll stay here in the cell until an agreement is settled or until the cops come in. Whichever comes first! We won't let anyone hurt you or the Captain. The door stays locked and no one gets in unless we know them." I looked at him waiting for a response but he didn't say anything. I knew my words didn't give much hope. They rang false even as I said them. It was difficult to give hope and reassurance when the words had to get past the images of bloody bodies and some son of a bitch with an ax. As I watched him, waiting for more words, he sat the cup down on the floor, leaned back against the wall and shut his eyes. The pain pills were starting to work. Maybe he'd sleep now and leave me alone with all the questions I couldn't answer. Hell, we were in the same boat. I didn't know from one minute to the next what was gonna happen. All the niceties of society didn't apply in there. No laws, no rules. Just survival of the strongest, the lowest denominator.

Glancing over at the Captain, I wondered what was going through his mind? Was he . . .

"Bang-bang-bang!" I spun around, jerked my knife out of my belt, and faced the door. Then three more sharp raps on the door and a voice said, "It's me, open the door, open the door!" I quickly took two steps to the door and pulled the curtain back, peering out the window.

"Ahh shit!!" I said. It's Weasel. What the hell was he doing back here by himself? I fumbled for the knob to unlock the door. As soon as I heard it click, he jerked the door open and rushed in. And before I could ask, he spewed out what they had found. "We were going into my unit," he said. "We heard screaming upstairs in B-2." He took a deep breath and rushed on. "We found three dead guys, blood all over the place. One guy was hurt bad and Stanley thought he had the nut trapped in the TV room!" The nut, the nut, trapped, they got him trapped . . . He went on, "They sent me to get you to see if you think we need help?" I quickly asked him, "Is it the nut, are you sure it's the nut?" The anticipation of getting some revenge for what indignation John went through lit fires in my mind. Weasel said, "Stanley thinks it's the nut they've got trapped in the TV room!"

I turned to the hostage Diego and told him that we'd have to leave him alone for a little while. He sat on his mattress wide-eyed since Weasel had burst in with the news. I also told him not to open the door unless it was one of us. He nodded his head in agreement.

I quickly took my pipe from Weasel and retaped it to my hand. I asked him, "Did you see any movement in the hallway?" He said, "Just lights further down the other way . . ." I nodded my head and said, "We'll do this ourselves, we don't need help!!"

Before leaving, I snatched the radio out of the socket and stuck it in my back pocket.

10 Something in the Dark

Leaving the cell, I shut the door and I heard the guard lock it but I still gave a hard yank on the handle to be sure. With Weasel in the lead, we plodded quickly down the tier to the stairs.

It was pitch black except for the flashlight that Weasel carried. He kept swinging it back and forth as he walked. We trooped down the stairs and stepped out into the ankle-deep water.

My thoughts were on the nut they had trapped in the Dorm B-2 TV room. I didn't believe we'd need any help in delivering some vengeful retribution on this guy. This was gonna be for John. Yeah, this was for John.

We turned to the left, wading out of the cellblock. I glanced both ways and saw no other lights in the long hallway and just the sound of our splashing steps echoed back at us. Weasel continued in the lead down the center of the water-flooded corridor.

Near the wall on our right, the glare from Weasel's flashlight danced over a body that looked familiar. I asked Weasel to hold up a second and shine his light on the form laying facedown in the water. I could tell from the long, curly blond hair that it was Shaggy and when I kneeled down to turn him over, it was obvious that he'd been murdered. The entire left side of his face and head had been bashed in. I looked into his dead face and muttered a disgusted obscenity at finding him this way. Just a few hours ago he had been alive, and if he had stayed with us he'd be alive now. But now he was beyond any help I could give him. I stood up and said to Weasel, "Come on, let's go. We can't do anything for him." I stepped away, shaking my head, and we continued on.

We passed three or four more bodies laying in the water by the wall. Weasel kept the light moving around and ahead of us, constantly probing the darkness for objects in our path. I couldn't keep myself from looking at the bodies we passed, looking for some recognition of who they were, but I didn't know any of them. At least not knowing any of them was some relief.

When we reached the grill bar gate at the bottom steps leading up to Dorm B-2, I hesitated before passing through the gate. I wasn't gonna be trapped behind a locked gate again, but I didn't have to concern myself with this one. Someone had used a cutting torch on the locking mechanism and it wouldn't have locked again until serious repairs were made.

We moved up the stairs and down a short hallway between the shower on one side and restroom on the other and to the dorm entrance. At the far end of the dorm I could see a light moving around where Stanley and Boots were leaning against a pile of bedframes they had stacked in front of the closed TV room door. Off to the left I saw movement where Frank leaned over someone in a bed. We walked on into the barn-like structure of the dorm and Weasel shined his light around into the darkest shadows. The room was crammed full of double-decker beds that mostly laid on their sides. There were five or six large piles of mattresses in different locations, as if someone had made their own super king-size beds to lay on.

The dorm was originally designed to hold 45 beds, but with the stacked double bunks. It now held well over 100 and that meant that more than 100 men were assigned to this dorm. All their meager belongings lay scattered everywhere—letters, pictures, clothes, and bedding were spread around like a storm had struck the room. Splashes of blood lay on everything. Puddles of it lay on the floor and smears of blood ran down a large center post that supported the ceiling roof.

Weasel's light darted back and forth, flashing over the mess that we walked through toward the TV room. With all the blood it looked like someone ran around bleeding on everything. Then his light hit a body and another one next to the first and another one just beyond. They each laid in puddles of blood where they'd fallen and bled out. It's obvious what probably happened here. All three bodies had deep, grisly cuts down their backs.

Stepping around the wet puddles and bodies, Stanley said in an excited voice, "I heard someone there . . ." He pointed his light at the barricaded door and I stepped over beside Boots and tried to see into the TV room through a wall of windows. All I could see was my reflection and large gouts of wet blood streaked across the glass.

Stepping back, I turned toward Frank and asked him if any of these guys on the floor were alive. He shot back with, "This man in bed is the only one we found alive but we gotta get him to the front. I can't get the bleeding to stop." Stanley and Weasel had their flashlights on the guy in bed. He had a waxy, pale white complexion, wrapped in white bandages from neck to stomach. From the wet, red places on the wrappings it was easy to see he'd been cut-chopped from his shoulder to his arm pit. His eyes were open, looking into the light with pain, fear, and panic. The blood on the bed and floor around him gave a clear picture of what indeed had happened here. He'd probably been attacked while laying in bed. Needles and other drug trash was scattered on the floor around the bed. All these guys had probably been partying or passed out or were just too stoned to defend themselves.

Turning back to Stanley I said, "Let's get some more steel before we open that door. I moved over to one of the bunk beds that had been tipped on its side. I used the pipe I had and beat off a piece of angle iron that was welded on the bedframe as a brace. It took a half-dozen, full-force swings to break one end loose while Stanley bent it back and forth to get it free. I broke another one loose for Weasel. They each had pieces of four-foot angle iron to use as clubs.

All three of us lined up in front of the door. Boots started dragging the bed-frames to the side, one at a time, from the door. When he had the last one out of the way, Stanley and I leaned our shoulders against the door to keep it closed. Frank took the two flashlights and stood behind us, shining the lights over our shoulders. I had my left hand on the door handle and my feet planted in between the splashes of blood on the floor. I asked if everyone was ready and said, "Now!!" Stanley jumped back and I jerked the door open wide. We all stood there with our weapons pointed and poised, ready for whoever came rushing out at us. We stood there shaking with anticipation for about five to eight seconds, waiting, expecting someone to jump out. But no one rushed at us and I edged closer to the entrance. Frank moved up and shined his light around inside the TV room. It was empty of any threat—just a steel picnic table, a smashed television in the corner, and two more bodies of recently killed convicts. One body was under the table, and from the blood smears on the floor, it looked like he'd dragged himself across the floor and under the table for safety and had bled to death. The other body laid on a blood-soaked mattress near the far wall where he'd probably been asleep. Both bodies had been cut and hacked on, similar to the others out in the dorm. Frank checked both bodies for signs of life but they were both dead. Everyone else stood in the middle of the room looking at one body and then another one. Stanley said offhandedly, "Man, I swear I heard movement in here." I pointed at the body under the table and said, "You probably heard him crawling on the floor or dying." He stepped over to the blood smear and scuffed his boot through it. It was still wet, too, which further confirmed how recently this had all happened. Frank stood up from checking the body under the table and said, "We just missed catching the nut doing all this." He trudged past me and out into the dorm where the live convict still laid on the bed. I followed him, asking, "What made you guys come up here in the first place?" He indicated the wounded convict on the bed and said, "We heard him hollering and followed the sound of his screams up the stairs." I looked down at the guy on the bed. He breathed fast, short breaths, panting, rolling his eyes back and forth like a frightened animal, looking at Frank and then at me. I asked him, "Do you know who did this to you?" He appeared to be looking at me or trying to focus his eyes on me. When he opened his mouth to speak, he only groaned and croaked unidentifiable words. I moved a little closer and said, "Come on man, who cut you?" He growled something deep in his throat and I could see the cords tighten on his neck as if he was trying to talk. Then the bandage around his neck suddenly soaked through with blood and Frank said, "Leave him alone. He's almost dead already!" He pressed a piece of towel on the bleeding wound. Frank looked up at me and said, "We gotta get this guy to the front or he's gonna die!" He pressed on the wound with one hand and pressed his knee into the left shoulder while reaching across the guy and pulling on the right shoulder toward his knee, effectively pulling the wound together to stop the bleeding. Frank continued holding the guy in a semi-bear hug and as the rest of us gathered around the bed he said, "As soon as I get the bleeding stopped, we need to wrap him as tight as we can in one of those blankets." He held the guy for about 30 seconds and when he released him, he sat the guy up in the bed and quickly wrapped the folded blanket around his shoulders to continue the pressure in holding the wound together. When that was done, we laid the guy on the other blanket. With the four of us carrying him, we skirted around the overturned beds and the trashed dorm to the stairway.

We carried him down the stairs and at the bottom landing, just before stepping out into the water, I said that we should hold up there and get some help. I didn't want to be hindered in carrying this guy and not be able to protect myself if attacked in the long open hallway. Stanley, Weasel, and Boots stayed with the hurt guy and Frank and I stepped out into the hallway. I pulled out our copy of the coded areas from my pocket while Frank held the light, I found Dorm B on the papers. The coded words beside it said, "Soap Box." I jerked the radio from my back pocket, twisted the on switch for more volume and thumbed the transmit button a couple of times to be sure it worked. Then I lifted the gas mask off my face and spoke slow and clear into the side of the radio. "Chopper One. Chopper One. I'm with the medic at the Soap Box." When I let my thumb slip off the button I got an immediate response from the radio speaker. "I hear you. What's the problem." I waited a couple seconds expecting more to be said but when nothing else came I thumbed the button again and said, "We found some nut cases in the Soap Box and need a hand in getting one out!" I tried to be as short and cryptic as possible so only the intended listener would understand my meaning. He did 'cuz he came right back with, "We'll be there in a few!" Frank let out an audible sigh of relief and said, "I'm sure glad there's a few of us working together to get through this madness." I could see only his silhouette in the darkness. We stood there like shadows, more substance than shape. I watched a shimmer on the water as it rippled away from where we stood. Further out, though, the darkness enveloped around us in almost total blackness. Looking out into it and in the direction of the prison center far down the hall, I thought how ironic. All our lives we teach ourselves not to fear the darkness because it's just darkness. But now there was something out in that darkness, something very menacing and deadly. A chill ran down my back. Then way down the hallway four lights came into view and they were coming our way.

Frank and I waited where we stood. As the lights came nearer we could hear their splashing steps. Frank winked his flashlight on a couple of times and we got a response flash. Then out of the darkness Felix came into view with six of his crew and immediately asked what we'd found. While Frank explained to Felix, I showed Lucky and the others where the injured convict lay on the stair landing. Stepping back out of the way so he could be brought out, they passed me and started down the hallway. With two of Felix's crew in the lead, six people carried the hurt guy and I waded behind with Frank and Felix. He told us about finding other injured convicts that he and his crew had taken to the front. We listened as he described the wounds of those that survived. A couple of the survivors had described and confirmed the nut as a tall, black dude and there was an organized search for him in progress now. A search that was concentrated on the North Wing. But as soon as they finished the other end, they'd start on this end, the South Wing of the prison. Frank explained that the killings were fresh in Dorm B-2, and he thought the attacker was still on this South Wing somewhere. I didn't say anything, just listened and followed the group in front of us.

We passed Cellhouse 1 where I'd left the two hostages by themselves. I didn't know how well it would be taken or accepted that I'd left them alone so I didn't say anything about it. I knew that Captain Vasquez couldn't and probably wouldn't go anywhere. I wasn't so sure about the other guard. I hoped that he would stay put. I wondered if he was brave enough to wander these hallways alone. Then I dismissed the thought because he knew he was safe in that cell and he knew about all this killing madness out here. I knew he'd be there when I got back.

We passed the dining hall and picked up four more convicts in Felix's group. They had been guarding the back dock to the kitchen to prevent anyone from leaving the prison and to stop those convicts out on the ball field from coming back in to steal food. Those convicts that had given up and had gotten out had been herded to the recreation ball field. They had been out on that ball field since yesterday morning. Recently they had been sneaking in through the back kitchen dock for food. It was a general consensus of those convicts still in the prison that those convicts who had run out earlier didn't deserve to be allowed to come back in for food or anything else they left behind.

We continued on through the gates around the control center and up the hallway where the administrative offices were smoldering piles of ash. All these offices had at one time or another contained all the paraphernalia and knick-knacks of years of accumulation. Now they held absolutely nothing of recognizable shape; just scorched concrete walls and piles of burnt debris.

At the front lobby we ran into six more convicts guarding the entrance. There we waited while Felix stepped out to the sidewalk running to the front gate to get permission to haul out another convict.

11   Stalking the Stalker

It had gotten to be routine for four masked convicts to carry the injured from the lobby to the front gate. They laid the dying man on the sidewalk and hustled back into the lobby entrance.

I stayed in the darkest part of the trashed lobby while they carried the man we found in the dorm. Looking out through the lobby doors, the entire front was lit up from the perimeter lights on the fence and portable generators with banks of lights around the fence line. Just beyond the lights I could make out the battle dressed, helmeted National Guard standing shoulder to shoulder. It was a gut-wrenching sight to look into the faces of M-16-toting soldiers when all I had was a club and knife.

Behind me I could hear Felix explain his search plan for the black man to Frank and Stanley. That still didn't seem right 'cuz I didn't believe it was a black doing the killing. I hadn't seen any blacks since the beginning of the riot. I thought they had all gotten out. Blacks were only able to live in a couple of the dorms and just one or two of the cellblocks. Although blacks didn't represent the lowest *number* of inmates in the joint—there were fewer blacks than Hispanics or whites, but blacks outnumbered Indians—blacks were the objects of the most racial hatred. In there, blacks knew which way the wind blew and I just couldn't see it that one lone black man was creeping through the joint killing for no other reason than he could—unless one had snapped.

When the four convicts returned from the gate we all eased out of the lobby, trooping back to the center of the prison, leaving the four convicts watching the forces out front. At the control center Felix told two of his crew to stay at the hallway junction and keep watch both ways up and down the corridor for any blacks. He took two more of his crew and walked off into the darkness toward the North Wing. He said he had to find the group already searching that end of the joint. The rest of us filed in behind Lucky toward the South Wing of the prison. We were gonna start our search at the school and Dorm D and work our way back toward the center and meet in the middle somewhere with the other group searching. Everyone was determined to smoke out this nut. He had to be found . . .

I was fifth in line behind Boots and when we passed the gym and dining hall, I stepped up close behind him and said in a low voice, "Hey man, those hostages of ours are alone in the cell. Why don't you go up to the cell and stay with them?" He agreed and as we passed the cellblock entrance, he just stepped out of line and waded to the stairs and we continued on. No one would know I'd left the hostages alone.

On reaching the school entrance there was a wall of bars across the width of the hallway. The gate was open but in front of it there was a steel bedframe barricade that had been thrown up at the beginning of the riot. This was to prevent the forces outside from getting in. Since then someone had moved the bedframes to make a crawl space under the barricade. After shining our lights on the other side to make sure no one was hiding, we crawled through one at a time. I was the second to go through and it completely soaked me crawling the short distance under the beds in the six or so inches of water. When I reached the other side I immediately jumped up, not paying attention to my wet clothes, and shined my light around both entrances—the school on the left and Dorm D on the right. Lucky was the first to crawl through and now we stood facing the unknown as the rest of our search group crawled under the barricade.

When everyone was through on this side, Lucky told three guys to stay put at the barricade and the other six of us started in the school first. Just as we entered the first classroom, Weasel slid up beside me and whispered in my right ear, "This is the room where we got jumped for trying to find a way out." I looked over at him and said, "Hey brother, blow that off. We got other things to do!" and followed the rest of the group into the room. No one's hiding in here but there's the window knocked out where convicts had escaped the riot earlier. We entered each room with the idea that the nut was hiding and waiting inside. We checked each closet and every nook and cranny with our weapons ready. We made as much noise as we could in case the nut was in there. If we could spook him out, make him panic and show himself, we probably had a better chance of getting him before he could use that ax on any of us. At each school room door Lucky kept repeating the same threat. "If you're in here nigger, you better run!!" There weren't very many places to hide in the classroom and after 30 minutes of high-energy tension, we could relax a little. All we found was a bunch of wrecked school equipment. We gathered up at the narrow hallway between the classrooms and determined that he wasn't in the school. We then moved over to the Dorm D entrance. This dorm is where newly arrived convicts who had recently been sentenced to prison were assigned—the fish tank. It was fairly easy to search the open dorm. We checked under beds and in the TV room at the far end. We made a lot of noise and tipped over a few bunk beds. After a few minutes everyone trooped out without finding anything. By now everyone was talking loud to add to the noise and possibly frighten our quarry. We sounded more like a gaggle of geese than a search party bent on mayhem. When we got back to the barricade I told everyone to quiet down. I hissed, "It's okay to make noise for the effect of making this nut show himself, but you guys are turning this into a party." A couple of guys I didn't know started groaning that no one should tell them what to do. That they were tired of being told what they should or shouldn't do. Then before I could say anything else, Lucky told them, "You fools shut up. You're making too fuckin' much noise!" He stood glaring at everyone in the darkness and at the whiners. It got quiet and one at a time we crawled back through the barricade to the open hallway. Once there we pulled a couple of the steel beds into the crawl space and pushed the others on top to seal it from anyone else getting in or out. It would now take some serious effort to dismantle this barricade.

From the barricade we trudged down the hallway to the Dorm E entrance. At the Dorm E-1 we couldn't get in. Those Protective Custody convicts had jammed their beds against the door at the beginning of the takeover. From the way the beds were wedged against the door, no one else had gotten in either and we left it as we found it and moved to the stairs to Dorm E-2.

This was the dorm in which the takeover and riot had started. This was where those first four guards were snatched and beaten into submission. That seemed like weeks ago. The dorm was wrecked, all the lights were knocked out. Those long fluorescent bulbs lay shattered on the floor with that white luminous powder from inside the bulbs sprinkled on everything. It looked strange when light from our flashlights pass over the beds and floor. Everything kinda shined in the ghostly light.

We found two people in different places. One laid in bed and one lay naked in the shower. That first one Stanley spotted with his light under a blanket near the dorm wall. He thought he'd found the nut again. We all rushed over and when one guy jerked the blanket away, we saw that it was just a body of someone who'd probably O.D.'d on drugs. We were cautious and treated every ominous-looking pile of blankets or mattresses as if the nut was hiding under it. We checked everything in the TV room. But no one was alive in there so we marched out and down the stairs. At the bottom landing Lucky said, "We'll check B-1 first and you guys stay awake. We're gonna catch that nigger!" We followed him off the bottom steps into the water and out into the hallway. We continued on across the hall into the entrance of Dorm B-1. At the entrance we spread out. This one is even easier to search than the other dorms because most of the bunk beds had been hauled out to use in the barricade at the school entrance. But we still had to pull apart stacks of water-soaked mattresses and bedding. Three guys searched the restroom while a couple of others looked in the shower. The rest of us made our way to the back room and into the TV room. Someone said there were two bodies in the restroom. They looked like they had been killed. We all stood around in the wrecked TV room. Someone had started a fire on the steel picnic table. It was just smoldering remains of cardboard and cloth. I didn't know if it meant anything, but then I'm not a master detective either. We calmed ourselves at finding nothing and strolled out, Stanley swept the fire remains onto the water-covered floor. We all moved toward the entrance, not saying anything. I believed it was finally soaking into these guys' heads that we were on a deadly errand and any wrong move could have been a last one. We gathered for a second or two at the stairwell to Dorm B-2 and Lucky and I went first with Stanley and the rest behind.

Just as we reached the top of the stairs, the radio in my pocket started to squawk. "We found him in the Catholic chapel!!!!" Then again it said, "He's in the Catholic chapel!!" Lucky was the first to react. He took off on a dead run, passed me and everyone else, bounding down the steps shouting, "Come on. He's in the chapel!" We all immediately followed with the more eager and faster of us in Lucky's wake. For some it was easy to navigate the ankle-deep water. For me it was as if I had a shoe full of rocks. It was like a mad dash in slow motion. The tape on my right boot had loosened again and I shuffled along at the back of the pack. Stanley and Weasel hung back for me but I waved them on. Now that we knew where to find the ax-wielding nut, it wasn't necessary to watch my back. I'd be alright and they could run on toward the chapel.

The Catholic chapel was just beyond the burned-out Captain's office. It had a single, wide wooden door with some sort of stained glass design in the center. As I kinda hop-skipped up to the open door, I could hear loud shouts of accusations and threats from numerous voices inside. I brought my pipe up ready for battle as I took the last few steps around the door and into the entrance.

First thing I saw was a tall, black dude standing alone on a raised, dais-type platform at the front of the chapel. He was completely illuminated from the flashlight beams on him. I hobbled up the aisle between pews. This was a small-sized chapel with four to five short wooden seats on each side of the wide aisle.

I kept my eyes on the black dude as I moved forward. He had a large butcher's cleaver in both hands. He had them cocked back, ready to swing at anyone who came close enough. His back was to the wall beside the altar, and facing him was a crowd of 15 to 20 convicts in a half circle. Some held pipes and knives. Others had flashlights in one hand, a knife in the other. Some even had garden tools—shovels, rakes, and one convict in the half circle held a pick ax. It reminded me of a movie I'd seen in which all the townspeople and farmers were after Frankenstein. It was so crowded around the platform that they were bumping into each other while trying to close in on him.

I stood back with some others and kept my light pointed at the nut. At first I didn't know who he was, but when someone said his name, Reggie, then I remembered the stories I had heard about him. He was one of the notorious rapists that every prison has. He was convicted of kidnapping two sisters, holding them for days in his apartment. He only got caught when neighbors complained about the noise. One of those classic cases that psychiatrists base their theories on. Yeah, he was infamous alright. Kept on maximum lockup because of the many convicts who wanted to take his life.

Different people in the group kept throwing a steady harangue of threats at him. "We're gonna kill your black ass, nigger!" and "You're a dead nigger!" Almost like a chant.

He stood with feet spread, hopping back and forth across the corner of the dais. Every time he moved, the crowd around him shifted and moved a little closer. He slid over next to the altar and the lights moving with him shined on an effigy of Jesus on the cross right behind him. He kept glaring at everyone around him as if he was looking for a sign of weakness. He did look crazy, just to be blunt. His eyes were bugged out, red and rheuny from the strain. I could see the cords pulled taut in his neck as he kept a steady, hard grimace. Most of the lights on him were on his face and he'd swivel his head like a boxer to dodge the light and see the circle tighten in around him. I shined my light on his weapon. It had a 12-inch blade, thick and shiny. He must have wiped it after using it. He moved a couple feet from the altar and one guy in the circle made a fake dash in and out. Reggie swung at him and another guy leaped in from the other side before he could turn. Then the whole line swarmed in. A sudden loud "clanning" as the second guy caught Reggie in the side of the head with his shovel. I saw him bounce off the wall from that first blow and he was immediately hit again and knocked to the floor on his back.

I had a bird's eye view standing on top of a little wooden fence around the dais and altar with my flashlight on the rush of people on him. Two guys were on his arm that held the cleaver. It was pinned to the floor of the platform. Six others held his legs down and three others were straddling his chest, stomach, and hips. And every one of them was stabbing and cutting him wherever they could. He started to scream in an eerie wailing that hurt my ears. He didn't have a chance but then he didn't deserve one either. They kept stabbing him. Pipes and clubs were tossed to the side as he struggled and screamed, the steel continued to plunge in and out of his body. Then when he quit moving and started gurgling with his mouth open, one guy on his chest reached out and slit his throat. It didn't even bleed as you would expect, because he was dead already. The gurgling was the remnants of his last scream. One at a time they released his arms and legs and everyone stood back ready to pounce on him if he moved or twitched. After a few seconds it was obvious that he had gone to hell. One of the guys started cussing and limping away. "You stabbed me in the leg!" he said to his partner next to him. He limped out through the gate in the little fence and sat down on the front pew.

I stepped down off the fence to get a better look at this dead madman. The blood from his body had puddled around him from numerous holes and rips. Everything was deathly quiet and Frank was talking to the guy with the leg wound. There were about 20 of us standing there, looking down at the body. Somebody said, "How many did he kill?" Another voice said, "At least eight or ten." And more people crowded on the platform to see the object of our fear and hatred. How can one man embody such madness to take on the chore that he had? I knew why he lay there with his life taken, but what drove him to that end? I couldn't fathom the answer except for anger, hatred to the point of madness with no room for pity. Where does the thought come from to make a man kill and maim as he had?

Before I could get a grip on the idea of understanding the thoughts flashing through my mind, the one convict with a shovel pushed past us saying, "Get back, get back. I want the head!" "Ahhh shit . . ." I mumbled and backed away to the wooden fence to get some distance. He raised the shovel over his head as he stepped over the body to the other side and all in one motion, swung the blade edge into the neck wound. It made a wet, smacking sound, striking flesh. Once, twice, three times he swung and cut deeper into the same spot. On the fourth blow the head popped off and skidded across the dais, hit the fence, and rocked back and forth on its side.

Everyone got quiet, just watching. I looked from the head to the body and back again. This was sick. This wasn't real. No, this couldn't be real. My stomach rolled and tweaked. Then a much deeper thought whispered in my mind—this was like 'Nam, this was survival. And that thought actually brought a twinge that my body and gut felt. Now, maybe, this madness could be over.

As more people came forward for a closer look, I'd seen enough and stepped over and sat down on the fence and tried to concentrate on what Frank was doing to the hurt guy's leg. I needed to focus on some sanity or semblance of it. I could hear movement on the platform behind me and a snickering laughter over where the head lay. Then a dull "thunk-splat" sound and everyone started laughing around the chapel. I turned my head in time to see the head sail airborne over the altar like a chip shot and land on the floor on the other side. The guy with the shovel was grinning and standing as a golfer would following through with a swing. I couldn't help but grin 'cuz it did look funny. And everyone continued laughing at the scene of the gruesome humor. Then the fellow with the shovel in hand walked around the altar and kicked the severed head over and held it wedged against the floor and bottom rung on the wooden fence with his foot and jammed the shovel handle into the open mouth of the mutilated head.

I turned back to see Frank, applying the last strip of gray duct tape to the bandage on the accidental stab victim. He said something to the guy and helped him to his feet. As the hurt guy limped down the aisle, right behind him, the guy with the shovel strutted out holding the severed, bloody head aloft for all to see and yelled, "I'm gonna give it to the pigs out front!" With him about a half-dozen convicts filed out of the chapel and toward the control center.

I stayed put where I sat, watching others straggle out in twos and threes. Frank and I were the last ones left in the chapel. He stood up flashing his light around the room and made comment, "This is the only part of the joint not set on fire." I stood and pointed my light at the headless body still lying on the dais beside the altar. I didn't say anything, but why burn the place? It had been desecrated enough. The body laying there in a huge puddle of blood had debased whatever had at one time been holy in the chapel. Frank moved to the aisle and toward the door. I stood there for a few seconds wondering if there really was a holy place in prison. This place had all the trappings of such reverence, but it too was just another room in a much bigger, miserable place. And I hobbled after Frank out into the hallway.

12   Looking at the Dead

Making our way slowly up the flooded hallway, Frank made several comments about Reggie and his last moments of life. Listening to him, he sounded cold, unfeeling about what we had just witnessed. Sure, some idiots deserve killing, and he most certainly laid claim to meeting the reaper, but not to the point of mutilation, not like that. We slogged ahead watching the flashlights moving around in front of us. One nut had been eliminated, but that didn't mean the threat of insanity had been eradicated. We still had to be vigilant in what was going on around us.

Moving closer to the Cellhouse 1 entrance, Stanley and Weasel stood with a group of people I didn't recognize at first. Stanley had a flashlight pointed toward the water-covered floor, reflecting the light into the strangers unusual facial coverings. They each had some sort of colored rag around mouth and nose. Trudging up beside Weasel, I immediately recognized the voice of one in the group.

Robert and his younger brother Larry were Apache Indians from Arizona. Robert always talked foul about the State of New Mexico. He was an older man doing time for robbery. He coined a phrase by twisting the state slogan "Land of Enchantment" into "Land of Entrapment." I'd always liked that. The others with him were younger Indians; those were the real minority of the joint. I think those five youngsters were Navaho from the reservation in the far northwestern region of the state called Four Corners. I didn't know Larry or the youngsters, but Robert had lived near me before the riot. I'd always liked his brash humor and the stories he told about the traditional Apache people of Arizona.

He stood in the ankle-deep water on the other side of Stanley, telling him about where they had been hiding out from the beginning of the riot. "We were in the library" he said. "I figured it would be a good place to keep my brothers together until this bullshit was over!" He spoke fast, waving his arms around at six others around him. They kept shifting from foot to foot, glancing around at the darkened hallway behind them. He continued with, "We didn't know what was going on until some guys broke in on us looking for some black dude. They told us we couldn't stay

91

there. We heard what was said over the radio that someone had found him in the chapel. What was that all about?"

Stanley started to say something. Then one of the youngsters blurted out: "Did you see that head those guys were carrying on the stick? They went right by us." For a moment, no one said anything; what could be said?

Robert glanced over at the youngster and back at Stanley saying, "What's been going on man?" Stanley shook his head saying, "Man, you wouldn't believe the bullshit." His voice kinda trailed off, as if he couldn't form the words.

I pointed my light up the hallway behind them and said, "It's been touch and go since last night-ah, I mean yesterday, when this started, but check it out." Everyone turned in the direction my light shined and saw the body floating, grotesque in the flood water. Lifting the light a little, I shined it on another body further down the hallway against the wall. No one said anything for a second, just staring at the form laying in the distance.

I glanced at Robert saying, "There's been a bunch of killing, they're all over." I couldn't see expression on anyone's face, but I was sure there was surprise at my words and at what they were seeing.

We heard splashing steps behind us and when I turned, Felix and part of his crew walked out of the darkness. He started in with his next plan of action. "We need to check the units at this end of the joint to see if there's any more wounded guys." He looked around at every one of us standing there. We were all staring at him as he spoke.

Noticing Robert for the first time, Felix said, "So that was you hiding in the library." Robert came right back with, "We weren't hiding, we were just waiting for all this bullshit to be over." Felix didn't say anything to that. But he did say, "Are you gonna help or go wait somewhere else?" Robert held his hands out and said, "We'll help!" Felix turned and started to walk away but stopped, saying, "Don't use the radios and don't turn on any lights, just use your flashlights. If you find anyone, bring them to the front. Then he walked on toward the control center.

I glanced over at Robert and said, "It looks like you've been drafted." He asked, "What's he talking about wounded?" I could see the puzzled expression on his face from the reflection of light off the water. "We already hauled one guy out a couple hours ago, he'd been cut on by the black that was killed in the chapel. There's probably more and we've only checked a couple of the dorms."

Turning toward Frank, I said "Where do you think we should start?" He handed his flashlight to Robert saying, "Might as well start here in Cellhouse 2. I'm going to the cell to check on the hostages, if you need me, send someone to get me." And he walked off in the darkened interior of Cellhouse 1. As he waded through the open gate I said, "Tell Boots to come down with his flashlight. We'll need him too. Robert and the troop of youngsters splashed in Cellhouse 2. I could hear Robert say something about checking his cell. Watching them wade through the water that covered the first floor, I thought how lucky they were. They were gonna see what the rest of us had to stomach. Robert took the group to his cell and stood there with the door open, looking in at the flooded mess that used to be his home.

From behind me, I heard Boots coming out of Cellhouse 1. As I turned he said, "Did you guys find that nut? Frank said you guys are looking for more people. What's going on?" Not saying anything, I turned back toward Cellhouse 2 and waded into the entrance, with Weasel, Stanley, and Boots following.

Stepping to the door of the first cell, I pulled open the door and shined my light inside. All I could see was the steel bed, desk, and green, plastic-covered mattress laying on the water-flooded floor. Letting the door swing shut, I moved to the next cell door. It looked the same as the first, a bed, desk, and water-covered floor. Turning toward my friends, I said, "Let's spread out and check all the cells." And I moved on to the next cell. Stanley and Boots waded to the other side of the tier and started looking in those cells as Weasel and I splashed from cell to cell on the side we were on.

At the next cell door, Weasel pulled the door open and we both saw the body on the bed. I stepped over closer to see if I knew the guy, but his face wasn't familiar and he was definitely dead. I didn't see any wounds on him, and when I rolled him over a syringe dropped onto the mattress. I glanced at Weasel saying, "He's O.D.'d himself!" Then I noticed the light blue tint to his face, an obvious indication of drug overdosing. Stepping back, I said, "Man, I bet there's a bunch of these in here." Then I turned and left the cell.

As we waded to the next cell, I noticed Robert and the youngsters had moved to the second tier, above us. They were going from cell to cell as we were. Hopefully we could get this done quickly and get back to the safety of our cell. I didn't feel comfortable wandering around looking at the dead.

As we came out of the next cell Robert hollered from the second tier, "Hey, we found one up here!" I took a couple steps out from the second tier walkway and shined my light up at Robert and the one of the youngsters holding a short Chicano man between them. Puzzled, I asked, "What's wrong with him?" Then looking closer, I could tell that something wasn't right with him. Robert said, "He was laying on the bed with another guy, the other guy's dead. They look like they been partying, there's pills all over the floor."

Wading toward the back stairs, I bounded up them two at a time, and almost stumbled over two bodies setting on the steps. It was the two guys who'd been robbing cells earlier. I didn't need to check them for life. You could see they had bled-out where they sat. Evidently, they had crawled to the steps after they'd been kicked off the tier. I moved around them without a second glance.

On the second-tier landing, I trudged down the tier to where Robert and the youngster were. "What do we do with him?" Robert asked. Looking closer at the guy they held up, I said, "Can he walk? Just walk him around a little bit, he'll come out of it." Robert had one arm and the youngster had another; they walked the semi-conscious man down the tier. They had to half-drag the guy, trying to get him to put one foot in front of the other. I followed their movement with my light. I hadn't seen it done before, but I'd heard that you could walk a drug overdose around until he came out of it. They took him to the end of the tier, turned, and brought him back towards me.

Shining my light into his face, I could see that he still had that stupor expression pasted across it; as if he was unaware of what was being attempted for him. "Let's put him in the shower, cold water will bring him around." They turned him around and started down the tier again toward the shower. I followed, thinking about what I'd heard for people who overdose on downers. I wasn't sure, but I thought I'd heard that a cold shower will bring the person out of it.

Walking around the end of the tier, I continued following them to the shower alcove. Weasel walked behind and he asked, "Should I get Frank?" I kept following and said, "Naw, we'll see if the cold water revives him first. If it don't, we'll take him to the front."

At the shower, Robert and the youngster lifted the guy over the small dividing wall. Robert kept talking to the guy or trying to get some response from him. But the guy only grunted in protest as they laid him on the tile floor and turned on the shower.

I stood on the tier looking at the guy, waiting for some kind of reaction, but there was none. He just laid there without moving while the water beat down on him. When I shined my light into his face, his eyes didn't react and as the water soaked through the shirt on his chest, I couldn't see any change in his breathing. I could barely see any movement there. "Leave him there for a bit, let's see if he comes to." I said.

Robert and the youngster stepped out and we all stood there on the tier, pointing our lights at him. Robert asked, "Do you know him?" I shook my head and said, "I don't remember him living in the cellblock before, I don't know who he is." In prison, it's like living in a big crowded city; you see a lot of people around you, but you don't know everyone and very few of those you do see, you remember or want to know.

Stanley and Boots came up the stairs on our right, and Stanley said, "We didn't find anyone alive downstairs, but there are a few bodies." He glanced in at the guy on the shower floor saying, "Who's that?" One of the youngsters said, "I don't know his name, but I think he lived in F-1 dorm." Everyone standing there pointed their lights at the man on the shower floor. But the cold-water soaking didn't seem to rouse him.

"We better take him to the front," I said, "it doesn't look like he's coming to." I stepped into the shower and shut the water off. "You other guys go ahead and check the other units. Stanley, give me a hand with this guy." Looking down on him, I noticed that he seemed to be turning a little darker shade of blue. I couldn't determine if he was breathing or not. I bent down and pulled the unconscious man up to the sitting position. Stanley moved in on the other side and got a grip under his arm. We lifted the guy to his feet, and he made a sudden gasp of breath. For a second there, I thought he was coming out of it, but he just hung between us, breathing slowly through his mouth. We carried him out of the shower and stood with him on the tier making adjustments. Looping his left arm over around the back of my head, I held onto his wrist with my left hand. Stanley, on his right side, did the same with his right arm and it lifted the guy off the floor between us. We carried him this way to the stairs.

Stanley went first, and sideways we slowly carried the guy down from step to step. Every so often the guy would mumble something that I couldn't understand. At the bottom we stepped out into the flood water and stopped to get a better grip on the guy. His feet barely skimmed the top of the water as we moved along.

Weasel, Boots, Robert, and the rest of the group followed us out into the hallway. I asked Weasel to come with us to provide light. He fell in beside us, shining his light out in front, guiding us around obstacles and trash in the water. Boots walked beside him, pointing his flashlight further down the darkened hallway. Robert and the group of Indians went the other way toward the F dorms.

We passed the chow hall entrance and could still hear water squirting from the broken pipes and appliances inside. We passed the darkened gym and the burned out, smoldering captain's office. On toward the control center, we passed other familiar doors and rooms.

I had my gas mask perched on top of my head and I could smell the smoke that continued to drift by from the smoldering fires that weren't quite out yet. The only sounds we heard were the splashing steps of our own feet.

As we neared the control center, we saw some other people coming toward us from the North Wing of the joint. Stanley and I stopped as they got closer. I immediately recognized Lucky and he was strolling along with some strangely dressed individuals. They looked like a rock-and-roll band coming on stage. What the hell is going on with these guys?" I thought. Then I recognized Bear. He and Lucky were grinning like the Cheshire cat. Bear had on a silver-glitter jacket. They stopped in front of us and three other equally weird individuals trooped up behind them. Stanley and I just stared at the whole bunch. One wore a bright, lime-green jacket. Another slid up with a velvet blue, high-collared cape around his shoulders. He slung it out to his sides as he stopped. The last one stood there with a shiny yellow jacket draped across his shoulders. I had to ask, "Where did you get the snappy threads?" Lucky stepped to the side and threw his hands out like he was introducing the next road show act for us. Bear did a kind of macho pirouette spin and everyone broke into laughter. While laughing, I had to tell him, "Man, you stand out like a lighthouse signal for boats." He just grinned for the show. Boots and Weasel kept their lights on his jacket, and the reflecting light bounced off the floor, ceiling, and walls around us. Surely these guys knew how ridiculous they looked in their getups. But then, Bear didn't care; it was all for the laugh, for the moment.

Lucky stepped in closer, looking at the man we held, saying, "What have you got here?" I shook my head and said, "We found this guy in Cellhouse 2, I think he's O.D.'d on something. We tried to revive him, but he just groans at us." Lucky shined his light in the guy's face and asked, "Who is he?" And kept his light on the face. "No one knows his name, but one of the Indian youngsters said he lived in F-1 dorm," Stanley said.

Bear quickly asked, "Where are those Indians at?" I said offhandedly, "They're checking F dorms now."

Lucky continued looking over the guy we held between us. "We'll take him from here" he said, and he and Bear moved over and took his arms. Bear said something to the guy in Spanish, but didn't get any response.

We watched as they carried the man through the control center gates. The strangely dressed group filed silently past, following behind Lucky and Bear. I shook my head at their crazy clothes, and we turned and headed back toward the units.

13 Killing for a High

Moving back up the hallway, we passed the flooded gym. I noticed movement inside, actually I saw lights, but didn't think much about it. We continued toward the units.

Just past the entrance of Cellhouse 2, we stopped to look at two bodies lying partially submerged, facedown in the water. One of them was Shaggy and when Stanley turned him over and recognized him, I heard an anguished mumble, "Ahh man . . ." at discovering another of our friends this way. Shaking his head, he turned the body over and we waded on toward the dorm entrance.

At the entrance to Dorm F-1 there were three bodies laying on one side of the vestibule leading into the dorm. As our lights passed over them, I noticed that two had wire loops around their throats.

One looked familiar but I couldn't put a name to the face. I asked Boots if he knew them, 'cuz this was the dorm he lived in before the riot. They looked young and I figured they lived there, but he said he didn't know them.

We waded on into the dorm and found it deserted. Robert and his crew of youngsters were nowhere to be seen and we spun right around and headed toward the stairs for Dorm F-2. Strolling up the steps, I heard Weasel complain about his water-soaked feet. Making the first turn in the stairwell, I heard loud, angry voices from further up. We hurried our pace to the top. At the head of the stairs I passed a body with no clothes on, and the voices from inside the dorm got louder.

In rounding the corner into the dorm entrance, I could see lights moving around the TV room at the far end of the dorm where the shouting came from.

It had started to get light enough to see the interior without flashlights. As I scrambled around overturned beds and mattresses, I thought it strange that the TV room would be so dark while the outside pre-dawn lit the dorm around us.

Just then one of the young Indians came stumbling out of the TV room doorway holding his stomach. Running past him, I could see blood streaming between his fingers and down the front of his pants.

When I burst through the door of the TV room, I immediately saw the silhouettes of Robert and Larry on my right, fending off three guys with knives. This room was pitch black except for the flashlight beams jumping back and forth across the ceiling and walls. The flashlights were all that Robert and Larry had to fight with.

Edging a little closer toward Robert, I could see from the corner of my eye Stanley, Weasel, and Boots trail in. Then I saw the screaming youngster on the floor. I heard him more than I could see him. He bellowed a steady line of profanities at the three with knives. The way he held himself, he acted like he'd been stabbed. On the far side of Larry, the other three Navaho youngsters were waving some sort of cloth material at the attackers, yelling and trying to distract them. The three with knives didn't pay any attention to me or the others that came in behind me. They were slashing and stabbing at Robert and Larry who stood straddle-legged around the youngster on the floor to protect him.

Stanley moved up beside me on my left and we side-stepped over to Robert's left side. At that moment, Weasel and Boots yanked the blankets covering the windows and the room flooded with hazy light.

The three attackers gave a shocked double take at seeing us move toward them. The one closest to us pivoted on his right foot and lunged at my face with his knife. I had my pipe up and jabbed out and ducked at the same time. His forward momentum jarred my arm all the way to the shoulder when my pipe caught him in the lower middle chest. His knife swept past not even coming close and I heard the breath explode from his mouth as he suddenly jacked over double. Robert leaped forward and smacked him in the side of his head with his steel flashlight and he slammed over on his side. I heard his knife spin across the floor.

The other two attackers immediately gave ground and we moved forward after them. Out of the corner of my eye I saw Stanley crack the one on the floor as he tried to get his feet under himself. Then the other two broke and fled behind the steel picnic table.

Robert shouted at them, "Come on you sons of bitches. You started this. Let's get it done!!"

They stood on the other side of the table glaring at us. The steel tabletop was littered with an assortment of drugs, little piles of colored pills, vials and needles, and other drug paraphernalia.

Everyone was breathing hard and we started around the table. Robert and Stanley went left and Larry and I went around the right. Robert hopped up on the tabletop to cut off any escape and we edged a few steps closer. Stanley still had his four-foot piece of angle iron and with the four of us moving in, the attackers didn't know which way to run.

Then one of them spoke out, "Go ahead, you can have our stuff. Go ahead and take it."

We all hesitated, looking at each other. I flashed immediately what this was all about. These assholes thought Robert and the youngsters came into take their precious drugs.

I started to say something but Robert kicked the pile of drugs off the table at the two idiots and said, "We don't want your fuckin' dope!" and stomped on the vials nearest his feet. He growled at them, "You bastards stabbed two of my brothers for this shit!!" He was obviously working himself up and continued kicking the pills and needles toward the two, now frightened, convicts. They stood with their backs pressed against the wall with a mixture of fear and dumbfoundedness as Robert destroyed their high and kicked the fragments at them.

He suddenly stopped, leaned forward toward them with a menacing leer, in a low, calm voice he said, "We don't want your dope, but you stabbed my brothers and you gotta pay . . ."

I moved forward a step when I thought Robert was getting too close to them, the way he leaned toward them, almost whispering to them. They changed from pale white to wide-eyed fear at his demented growl.

I didn't see any need for taking this any further and said, "We don't need to kill them. This is just a misunderstanding . . ." Both of the idiots started nodding their heads in full agreement with my words. I glanced at Robert and he shook his head with anger and anticipation, still glaring at his two frightened enemies.

Stanley quickly said, "We can blow this off 'cuz these guys don't want to fight anymore . . ." Larry came right back with, "As long as they drop the knives." The two immediately let their knives clatter to the floor at their feet and held their hands out to show they were empty.

I looked again at Robert. He let a grin slide across his mouth, but his eyes were cold, calculating—watching the two weaponless fools. Then he stood up straight and said offhandedly, "All right. Get your stinking asses out of here." Stanley moved back a couple of paces and motioned for them to come out on his side of the table. Larry and I moved forward to herd them on around. They got the idea and started in the desired direction.

They were watching Stanley as they side-stepped around the table end. When the first one passed under Robert, he swung his flashlight and busted the guy in the back of the head. The guy stumbled forward and Larry leaped past me and on the second guy with his flashlight. While Robert and Larry beat the piss out of the second guy, Stanley held the first on the floor with a foot on his back. They didn't need any help, so I just stood watching.

Finally I'd seen enough and started for the door. Walking past the one Stanley held on the floor, he whined, "I thought you guys said it was over . . ." I just stared at him walking by. From across the room Robert growled, "I didn't agree to anything and you gotta pay . . ."

I continued out of the TV room and into the dorm where Boots and Weasel stood over the two hurt youngsters. At first glance they needed more help than I could give them. I quickly told Weasel to go get Frank and for him to stay with the hostages. He took off like a shot through the dorm.

Kneeling down beside the first youngster, he had a towel pressed to his lower stomach. "Let me see," I said to him and he moved his bloody hand away. I lifted the towel, looked and quickly pressed it back down. He had a six-inch gash. He laid on his back on a stack of mattresses. Looking at his chalk-white face, his expression said, "Help me . . ." I pressed his hands harder onto the bloody towel and said, "Hold it tight." I stood up and glanced at the other kid. His bloody shirt hung open and I could see two puncture wounds seeping blood on the left side of his chest. Boots held a towel on his bleeding shoulder wound. I stepped over a little closer for a better look.

I could hear Robert and Larry still working-over the idiots in the TV room. You wouldn't believe that an 18-inch flashlight would make that kind of whacking noise hitting flesh.

Looking closer at the kid's chest wounds, they weren't bleeding like they should. And this youngster was not breathing right. He's panting. His lung's been hit or maybe his heart. I looked at his eyes. They were shiny bright and I knew this kid needed help fast.

I turned to see Stanley coming out of the TV room shaking his head. He had three kitchen knives clutched in one hand. He walked over, looking at the half-dead kid behind me. "How's he doing?" he said. "Not worth a shit!" I shot back and stalked toward the TV room door. I brushed past the three other Indian youngsters standing in the doorway watching the frenzy inside. Robert and Larry had beat one attacker to an unconscious, bloody mess. Larry worked on the other one behind the table. Robert stood over the one I knocked the breath out of. He was hitting the unconscious guy in the face like a trip hammer. I mumbled to myself, "That's enough . . ." Then I shouted, "Damn it, what's more important?" They both stopped their assault and looked at me as if I'd interrupted their meal in mid-bite. I glared back at both of them. "One of these kids is dying out here if we don't get him to the front, so what the fuck is more important? This???" I said pointing around the room. Then I turned and walked out.

Just then Frank came huffin' and puffin' air into the dorm entrance. He hurried to the nearest kid on the stack of mattresses and started working on him. He crooned and cadgered the youngster into sitting up so he could wrap some gray duct tape around his middle and a dry piece of torn sheet. He kept glancing over at the other, now-unconscious, kid. He reassured the kid with the gut wound and moved over to the next one.

Boots held the youngster sitting slumped on the floor. Frank got down on his knees and with fast, efficient moves, he stopped the bleeding on his shoulder. Working on the two chest wounds, he stopped two or three times to check for a pulse on the youngster's throat. He looked grim and kept working on the kid.

Robert and Larry came out of the TV room and stood beside me watching Frank work on the youngster. They didn't say anything until Frank stood up and announced, "We gotta get this man to the front or he ain't gonna make it." Robert jumped to gather blankets and with direction from Frank, they laid the unconscious youngster on two of them. The other said he could walk, and with help, he was pulled to his feet, holding his bandaged stomach. Robert and the other Indians started through the dorm with the kid on the blanket.

Frank turned to me and said, "Weasel told me there's a fight up here. What the hell happened?" I walked him to the TV room door and gave him a quick rundown of what took place. He looked at the three laid-out losers of the fight. He asked, "Are they dead? Did you kill 'em?" I looked in at them and said, "Yeah, they're probably dead, but no, they ain't mine . . ." He waved his arm at them and we turned to catch up with the rest of the guys.

We caught them at the stairs wrestling with the youngster on the blanket. Frank moved down in the stairwell to hold the kid on the blanket so they wouldn't dump him turning the corner on the stairs. Stanley and I helped the walking wounded down one step at a time. It was slow going, but we made it to the flooded hallway. Once there, the youngster we were helping along said it hurt too much to walk in the water. We had fallen behind Robert and the others with the kid on the blanket. They were quite a ways down the corridor already so we made a seat with my pipe. Stanley held one end and I gripped the other. The kid sat between us, holding on with one arm around Stanley's neck and the other holding his middle. We stepped out and the kid was light as a feather. We caught up with Frank and Robert at the control center gates.

Walking on through the gates, Frank kept pressing his fingers on the throat of the youngster on the blanket. Then we were in the short hallway with the burned-out offices and two convicts stepped out, blocking our way. Frank quickly said, "Where's Felix? We gotta get this guy to the front!" He continued walking toward the two blocking our path. Then further up the hallway Felix and Lucky came out of the visiting room door looking in our direction. Felix immediately said, "Let 'em by!!" He came toward us saying, "What have you guys found?" The two blocking our way stepped to the side and Robert and Larry continue with the kid on the blanket. We followed and listened to Frank explain to Felix what had transpired in the dorm.

We moved on through the visiting room and out into the lobby. Felix made for the door to get the go-ahead in taking the youngster to the front gate. Stanley, Frank, and I stood by the lobby doors as the youngster on the blanket was carried out. The kid we carried said he could walk the short distance to the gate and he followed behind the guys carrying the blanket.

I asked Frank how the kid on the blanket was and if he'd make it. Frank said in a flat voice, just barely above a whisper, "He's dead already. He died while we were coming down the long hallway." We continued watching them move along the sidewalk toward the gate without saying anything else.

They went through the routine of laying the kid on the sidewalk beside the closed gate and walked back to the lobby doors. Then the gate rattled open.

Everyone watched from the lobby as four state cops stepped in, lifted the blanket, and carried the kid about a dozen steps through the gate and laid him down. The other youngster was taken out at gun point and the gate rattle-slammed shut. The cops surrounded the standing kid, put handcuffs and leg irons on him and walked him around the building out of sight. They put handcuffs and leg irons on the dead youngster, rolled him over onto a canvas stretcher, and carried him away.

14   The Laughing Dead

Moving back through the lobby, visiting room, and smoldering administrative offices, I listened as Felix explained his strategy for the negotiations with Frank behind us. He planned to start the talks with the officials at 8:00 a.m. He said he wanted two, maybe three convicts to stand with him at the gate and witness what was said. I heard Frank say, "Uh-huh, uh-huh . . ." to every point in Felix's game plan. Then I heard them stop and Frank said, "Don't include me in on having to stand at the gate and listen to their lies . . . it just ain't for me." I turned my head to see Frank and Felix about a dozen steps behind us. I said to Stanley and Boots beside me that we should hold up for a minute. Turning back I heard Felix say something about finding someone else and he walked away toward the visiting room door. Frank turned toward me and waved his arm out saying, "Let's go on," and we continued in the direction of the control center gates. Ahead I heard Robert and Larry discussing whether that youngster they'd carried out would live or not. I pondered for a moment of telling them he'd died already, but I didn't say anything. They'd find out soon enough.

The flood water started deepest at the control center gates and we waded on through those and turned left. We still had a few more dorms to check, and we splashed down the center of the corridor. Moving along, I couldn't help noticing the strangeness in the water covering the whole floor—wall to wall as far as the eye could see up the hallway. It looked like a huge swimming pool in the light of day the way the light fluttered across its rippling surface.

We waded slowly past the chapel entrance on my left, the guard's chow hall on the right, the blackened, burned-out Captain's office and the gym. I had walked this walkway for the last three years and none of these rooms or doors held any real significance for me. But now, each one had import and a special memory. I glanced in at the gym interior. Someone had pushed all the bleachers to the center of the floor. I didn't pay it any particular attention and we trudged on past the doorway.

At the entrance of Cellhouse 1, Frank peeled off saying he would stay in the cell with the hostages. He also said in a grumbling voice, "You better be careful going into those units, there's still a bunch of nuts out and about." His voice kind of trailed of as he walked away to the cellblock.

The rest of our eight-man group kept right on to Dorm A-1. There I quickly explained, "We'll all stay together going into the units." Everyone stood staring into the dorm entrance, nodding their heads in agreement. Stanley handed Robert and Larry a knife, a piece taken from those idiots we'd left in Dorm F-2. He held the third one out in the direction of the remaining three youngsters and the one to grab it had a knife.

With everyone set, we crept into Dorm A-1 and spread out to sweep-search through the dorm. The tension rose when Boots found a suspicious group of bunk beds circled up with blankets thrown over them. The dorm was trashed out just like the others, bedding and personal items strewn around like a huge hobo camp and everything steeping the swamp, empty of life.

At the TV room we could see through the wall of windows that no one was lurking in the bushes inside. Stepping into the room, Robert and one of the youngsters went to a pile of bedding to see what it hid. It was nothing. We had to be on our guard constantly, though. At every turn, at every pile of mattresses, we had to assume there *was* something threatening lurking there.

A National Guard helicopter flew over-head and hovered out by the perimeter fence. I stepped over to the outside windows to see what it was doing. The chopper slowly circled twice and flew off toward the northwest. In the distance I could see lines of troops moving through the parking lot. There were still alot of spectators standing on the grass by the outside fence. They'd probably been there all night long. Stanley moved up behind me looking over my shoulder. "See those Army guardsmen," I said resignedly, "they're gonna storm in here on us. See how they're practicing those moves and getting it together?" I backed away from the window, pointing at the troops doing a tactical maneuver beyond the fence. "They're getting ready . . ."

I heard some of the other guys moving beds behind us in the dorm. Boots shouted, "There's someone under the bed!" I quickly turned, moving in his direction and forgot what was going on outside. Wading through the muck into the dorm again, suddenly one of the youngsters banged the door running out of the restroom saying, "The-the-there's a dead guy in there and he's grinning at me!" Larry said something in an exasperated tone and the youngster immediately hung his head and whispered something in his language in a low grunt. Larry took the kid back into the bathroom, admonishing him about his actions.

Boots and another of the young Indians dragged the bunk beds apart, and we all saw what was thought to be something hiding underneath. It was a fully clothed body. I glanced down at the ragged wound in the throat and blew air out of my mouth at the instinctual shock and from not wanting to inhale what my eyes were glued onto. Boots backed away saying, "He's a mess . . ." and threw a wet blanket over the body.

I followed Stanley when he and Robert passed behind me. Robert walked to the bathroom door, pulling it open and we all looked in at the dead man on the floor. In death he had a pleasant smile painted across his face. It was as if he was laughing at his own death. It looked strange the way his arms and legs stuck up in the air as if he was doing an imitation of a dying cockroach. One of the youngsters behind me asked, "Why do these guys turn blue when they die?" No one said anything. I turned to say something but it didn't seem important enough to waste the energy and I trudged away toward the dorm entrance.

At the stairway leading up to Dorm A-2, I stopped, waiting for the rest of the group. Stanley moved up beside me and I glanced over at him. He had his bar laid across his right shoulder like a baseball bat. With Boots and Robert behind us, we mounted the stairs in tandem sounding like a whole boatload of fishermen walking in holed waders; the way our water-soaked steps sounded. Stanley was on my right, and when we made the first turn in the stairwell he said, "I hear something. You hear that?" I did, and I stopped three steps from the top of the stairs, listening. I heard running footsteps and a murmur of words coming from around the corner in the dorm entrance. Whoever it was, surely they'd heard us coming up the stairs, and this was getting hairier by the second. My right foot was touching the step above, but most of my weight was on my left. I felt a shiver run up my right leg—anticipation, fear. I didn't like this . . .

At that moment Stanley leaped up the last few risers to the landing above. I bounded up the steps and rounded the corner beside him. Swinging my pipe up and out, I spotted two unknown armed convicts stepping out through the dorm entrance facing us about 30 feet to our front. They stood frozen, watching us through their towel masks. I heard and felt the rush of feet behind me as the rest of our group moved up the stairs to the landing.

Everyone at both ends of the short vestibule stood eyeing each other and I couldn't see but three people—the two at the door and one behind. In an even-modulated voice, "We're looking for anyone hurt. Is there anyone up here who needs to get to the front for help?" I said and stepped about three to four paces ahead, keeping eye contact with all three of them. Stanley moved up a few yards ahead of me. His eyes were bugged out, looking wild and ready for anything. As I took a few more steps, the three facing us backed through the entrance looking at me, Stanley and the six behind us and they continued backing into the dorm interior. They said something to one another in Spanish and the one standing at the back said, "Es'e, we no-wann-no trouble," in heavily accented English. Stanley and I kept moving forward until we reached the door. From behind me Robert said something in Spanish and the three strangers started shaking their heads in negative. I moved ahead stepping through the entrance on the left side of the door. Stanley stepped through on the right.

We stood in the dorm entrance, slowly checking everything in the early morning light. The bunk beds laid on their sides, and off to the left I spotted two naked guys, I assumed they were hostage guards. They were tied to a bed leg side by side, sitting on the floor with pillowcases over their heads. At that moment the first Chicano that spoke before said something and I understood Felix's name. Robert said in English, "They say Felix told them to watch these whore dogs." He indicated at the guards, flicking his hand at them. I glanced at the tied cops. They kept moving their heads as if they could see and the blood-spattered pillowcases flapped back and forth. I said to Stanley, "I don't see anyone hurt!" He glanced down his side of the dorm interior and announced the same conclusion. Then one of the other two Chicano's said, "Weee hab no siick ones here, Es'e . . ." I looked at the speaker and felt an instant flash of revulsion. He stood with his knife at ease and he wore the American Flag slit down the middle like a poncho. I started to make comment, opened my mouth and just snapped it closed and glared at the black orbs watching me through the mask. I don't know if he realized the disrespect he showed in what he wore. Out of the corner of my vision I saw Stanley turn away and step through the dorm door. I moved back a step and kept staring at the guy. When my back bumped the door jamb I turned and followed as Robert and Stanley leisurely walked toward the stairwell. I should have said something about the flag. I admonished myself. But then that would just get shit started and we weren't there to argue over a piece of cloth. Yeah, it was just a piece of rag, it didn't mean nothing to me. Moving down the steps I loosened the grip on my pipe. It's hard to explain to someone who hasn't been in the service what that flag represents. And even though I've not quite felt like an American ever since coming home from Southeast Asia, it still rankles to see Old Glory cut and worn like some fashion statement.

At the bottom of the stairs I stepped off into the water and moved around two bodies laying in the entrance. I glanced at them to see if I knew either and kept walking out.

At the entrance to Dorm B-1 we gathered for a moment and moved together through the doorway. We found nothing alive or dead in either the dorm or TV room. Stanley hollered from the restroom that he'd found two people in there. I waded through the muck into the back part of the restroom where the commodes were. There on the floor were two bodies. At first we thought one of them was alive, but when we turned him over, it was obvious he'd been dead for a few hours. Boots brought in a water-soaked blanket saying he knew one of them, and laid the blanket over him.

Moving up the stairway to Dorm B-2, we didn't expect to find any living, but we went through the motions of checking anyway. Walking through the dorm, I found a dry towel and wiped my hands on it as we looked through the TV room and bathroom. All we found were the bodies we'd seen before. No one said anything as we looked them over again.

Then as I followed the group down the stairs, Stanley stopped on the steps saying, "Man, there's alot of dead on this end of the joint. How many dead do you think there are?" I glanced at him without saying anything and kept stepping down the stair treads. "Have you been counting the dead, man?" he said behind me. I still didn't say anything and he kept on with, "I bet there's over 50 dead already. What do you think?" I kept moving downward a step at a time and as we took that last step, I mumbled, "I don't know man. I really don't want to think about it. Know what I mean, man?" He didn't say anything else about it and we waded out into the hallway.

Stepping into the entrance to Dorm E-1, I watched as two of the Indian youngsters pressed their shoulders against the barricaded door. Robert stood behind them saying, "Push, push, come on ppuussh . . .," but the bedframes on the other side of the door held it shut tight. "Blow that off," I said. "There's no need for us to get in there. Let the cops check that one." Stanley splashed up beside me and said, "There's probably nothing in there anyway. All those guys got out the windows." Robert stepped back from the door and peered in through the square windows around it and announced "I don't see anything." I turned on my heel saying, "Fuck it, let's check E-2 and get this over with."

The knowledge of this being the last unit to check seemed to lighten my water-logged step. I quickly ran up the stairway. Rounding the corner at the top steps of the dorm entrance, I heard water spraying from the shower room. I glanced in through the wall of windows as I passed and saw a naked guy laying on the shower floor. At first I wasn't sure what was going on, but when it was determined that no one laid in wait, I moved in the dorm and pulled the shower room door open. I could see the guy was dead from the way he just laid there, blue and unmoving. Letting the doors close, I started through the dorm toward the TV room.

Stanley was saying something about the shower as he came in through the dorm door behind me. I continued on between the overturned beds, looking at the piles of trash and discarded clothing on the floor. It wasn't any different than when we were up here before.

Moving into the TV room, I gave it a quick look-see and turned back toward the front of the dorm. I noticed everyone at the shower door when I came out of the TV room. Strolling in that direction I glanced at the body on the bed near the dorm wall. There was no need to look any further and at first I didn't know what the other guys were doing in the shower.

Then as I walked up behind Larry and one of the youngsters, two of the young Indians came out of the shower carrying the front half of a blanket with the naked wet man on it. Robert and Stanley had the other end of the blanket and as they came out, I looked closer at the blue-tinted face and said, "I think that guy's dead." Stanley quickly said, "He's breathing!" And handed the corner of the blanket to one of the youngsters standing there.

I walked along the side of the blanket, looking at the slow rise and fall of the guy's chest. At the stairway Stanley said, "At first I thought he was dead too, but they'll get him to the front." We stood at the top of the stairs and watched Robert and the youngsters carry the man down. They'd learned fast how to carry a body—ham-mocked between them. The weight is easy to swing around the narrow corner in the stairwell. Maybe not a very noble vocation, carrying bodies, but something done often enough they got the hang of it, so to speak.

15 The First Exchange

Stanley and I followed Robert and the youngsters down the hallway as far as Cellhouse 2. There they said they'd take the guy on the blanket to the front. Stanley and I stood there for a moment watching them trudge on down the long, smokey hallway. Then I turned and waded into the cellblock that I'd called home. I hadn't taken a dozen steps and realized that Stanley was right behind me.

Moving to the stairs, I announced that I was gonna get some clean clothes and take a shower and meet everyone at the house in Cellhouse 1. At the top of the stairwell, Stanley continued following. Rounding the corner on the second tier, I saw Boots and Weasel on the bottom floor walking out of the block. I assumed they were going to the cell where we kept the hostages. And I continued on toward my house.

Stepping into my cell I took a deep breath, glancing around at my sparse belongings scattered on the floor. I slowly let out the breath and limped on sore feet from the door to the desk, picking up my letters and pictures. At the desk I sat down on the metal stool, took another deep breath and laid the possessions on top. The cell thieves had cleaned me out of everything of value. Well, everything except my dry clothes. I reached into the metal cubby hole at the side of the desk and pulled out an old, but functional, sweatshirt, a clean pair of gray pants, boxer shorts and a couple pairs of dry socks. I had to look for a towel. It had somehow gotten tossed behind the bed but it was clean. I gathered everything in my left arm and headed for the door. On the way out of the cell I grabbed a bar of soap off the sink top.

Out on the tier I could hear a shower running. Yeah, I smiled to myself, Stanley was already in the rain room, and I headed down the tier in the direction of the sound. The shower was at the other end of the block from my cell. The same one in which we had revived the druggy from overdose earlier.

When I was about 30 feet from the shower alcove, a pair of wet, gray pants went flying out over the railing of the tier to the floor below. Then a wadded, blue shirt followed the pants.

Continuing on, I strolled to the shower opening and there stood Stanley buck naked under the water spray with a bar of soap in one hand and a knife in the other. "What the hell are you doing man?" I grinned at him. He laughed and coughed saying, "I think I'm gonna have to scrape this dried shit off." I saw what looked like dried mud all down his legs and on his stomach. It wasn't mud, though, it was dried blood.

I leaned back on the railing and waited. One of us had to watch while the other was vulnerable. I remembered how we use to do this in 'Nam. When we had been on patrol for any length of time, we'd be dirty and sweaty from humping through the heat and when we'd crossed a stream or pool of water, while half the squad stripped down and bathed, the other half would watch for the enemy. The only difference then and now is we don't need to be concerned about the black slimy leeches in the water. But compared to this right now, I'd much rather be back in Vietnam—leeches, gooks, and all. The riot, madness, and fear had no real comparison to that war. Vietnam was a walk in the park compared to these last two days. Actually, the only things that had any similarity between then and now were the abilities to adapt, survive, and not let some bastard get too close. The things I'd learned and lived through in that experience had helped me make the right decisions in this madness—that and a lot of luck.

When Stanley finished, dried off, and dressed himself in clean, dry clothes, we traded places. I stripped off my clothes, wet boots, and eased under the warm water. At first I didn't realize how difficult it would be to wash myself with just my left hand. So I soaked the tape loose on my right wrist and laid my pipe aside. Standing under the warm, soothing water allowed me to relax for a bit and it was like heaven to the feel the warmth return to my body. I stood there for the longest time before I started to soap up.

As I was drying myself, Stanley took my clothes and started shredding them with his knife. Before I could ask he said, "I'm cutting out the laundry numbers so the pigs can't say these are yours." I started to ask why, but what was the use? He flipped my pants over the railing and started cutting on my shirt. At that point I just nodded my head in exhaustion and continued drying off.

Sitting down on the small wall that separates the shower area from the walkway of the tier, I tenderly dried my feet. They looked like wrinkled prunes and felt like parchment paper and if I wasn't careful, I'd tear the skin.

Stanley stood over me saying something about the bodies. I barely heard him as I dressed and pulled my wet boots back on. Then he said something about "a point" and it grated a little deeper than his other utterances. I glanced up at him and asked, "What are you saying?" His voice filled with anxiety saying, "What was the point in killing all those guys . . . I just don't understand what the point was." I shook my head and said, "Brother, I don't know what the point or reason was for any of this," swinging my arm out behind me. "But I wouldn't trip on it, if I was you." I stood, reached for my weapon and stepped out of the shower saying, "Come on," and made my way to the stairway.

He didn't say anything until we were in the middle of the deserted hallway. "You know, we're accomplices in killing those guys in the dorm." I stopped in mid-step and turned on him. "What are you tripping on brother? We didn't kill anyone, and I'm damn sure not gonna say anything about those assholes in the dorm." I was trying to focus on his eyes through the gas mask lens, but all I could see was my own face in the reflection. We stood there facing each other over something for which we were probably culpable, but who was gonna say anything? I didn't know what else to say, but I said, "Man, I don't know . . . and at this point, I don't give a shit!" Shrugging my shoulders, I turned and walked into Cellhouse 1.

When Frank opened the cell door for us, I could tell that something wasn't quite right. Everyone in the cell sat listening with rapt attention to the continuous line of threats and verbiage over the two-way radio. Somewhere in the joint someone had a radio and in English the speaker said he'd kill anyone who released the hostages. Stanley and I stood just inside the door listening at each threat repeated three or four times. "What the hell is going on?" I said pointing at the radio.

Glancing around at the faces in the cell, all I could see was another round of hope shot down from their expressions. Frank said, "That's the fifth or sixth time that's been ran out over the radio." The expression on his face was pure disgust. "There was talking earlier about releasing some of the hostages, an exchange of some kind and then that shit started," he said. I shook my head in a kinda daze at first. Then I turned and twisted the lock on the door. No need to take chances now.

Turning back to the room, I watched Frank as he growled. "Fuck this, I'm gonna find out what's happening." He pointed at Stanley, "You come with me." And stepped past me to the door. "We'll find Felix and find out what's going on." He fumbled with the knob unlocking the door and said, "We'll be back as soon as we find something out," and he and Stanley were gone.

After relocking the door I turned to Boots. He had a bewildered expression painted on his face. Weasel sat on the end of the bed looking at the floor for his answers. The hostage guard, Diego, sat on his mattress against the wall. I couldn't read anything from his face. The white cream and swelling from the burns made that impossible. The Captain still laid where I'd last seen him with that same void stare in the one eye that wasn't swollen shut. The slight breathing and shaky movement of his chest were the only indications of life.

I tried to put a face to the voice that continued over the radio. If I knew who made the threats I'd know how serious to take them. It had to be someone with a group behind them. It had to be someone on the other end of the joint.

"What are we gonna do?" Weasel asked in a flat, unemotional voice. I glanced at him. He still stared at the floor, twisting the broken end of his steel bar into the concrete between his feet. All I could come up with is, "We wait." I looked at Boots and back to Weasel. "Do you recognize the voice on the radio? It sounds familiar, but I can't put a name to it." Weasel quit the grinding and said, "I think one was Felix." He looked up at me. "No, No," I said, "Not his voice, but that one now." I pointed at the radio. He just shook his head and resumed grinding into the floor. I glanced at Boots to see if he had anything to say, but he just stared back with that same waxy, white expression of fear that I'd come to recognize.

Not knowing what else to say, I glanced around the cell and spotted Frank's canvas bag laying on the end of the bed. Rummaging around in his bag I found the roll of gray duct tape on the bottom. It didn't take long to retape my shoe and reattach my pipe to my right wrist. With that done I felt ready for anything. Weasel took the tape and used it to shape himself a handle at the end of his steel bar. I took a couple of stay-awake pills out of my shirt pocket, popped them in my mouth and swallowed them dry. Then I squatted down to help Weasel fasten his bar to his right hand. As he tore tape off the roll, someone knocked on the door.

Slowly standing up, I moved to the door and pulled the towel cover back to look out of the window. The face on the other side was Stanley's and I quickly unlocked the door and stepped back.

As he pulled the door open he announced, "They're burning bodies in the gym." He quickly locked the door and went on. "I watched some guys from the other end of the joint carrying the dead into the gym." Everyone in the cell gave him their full attention. "They've already started it burning." I saw visions of a huge charnel pyre, and thought that would be a good way to get rid of all the dead. But why burn the bodies? Surely when the cops get back in here, they'd know who's missing. I glanced over at the guard sitting on the floor. He stared at Stanley. I wonder what he's thinking about all these new developments? The blank expression on his face didn't indicate any thoughts.

Turning back to Stanley, I asked, "Where's Frank?" Stanley just shrugged his shoulders saying, "I left him with Felix and some of the other guys at the control center." He moved over and sat down on the end of the bed beside Weasel saying, "Man, there's some shit going on at the other end of the joint, and all those bodies they took to the gym." He sounded more frightened by something. I looked from him to the others and the effect was catching; everyone seemed spooked by this turn of events.

Everyone got quiet and the radio became a steady stream of static. We were each kinda holding our breath for the next onslaught. I noticed the wisp of smoke floating up from under the door and watched it for a moment, then pushed a towel over with my foot and blocked the space between the floor and the bottom of the door. As I turned away, Stanley muttered, "It's gonna get alot worse, that gym was roaring when I walked by it a few minutes ago." I turned back to the door and lifted the window cover, looking out at the smoke-filled cellblock. Dark gray smoke completely cut off any view beyond the door.

As I stood there looking out, I saw Frank materialize out of the smoke. He was saying something to the guys behind him. I could just barely make out the shapes of four guys but I didn't recognize them. Frank glanced at the door and started to knock, then he saw me in the window and smiled in kind of a grimace. I didn't know what to think and said out loud, "We got Frank out here with four guys, get ready." And I unlocked the door. Behind me, I heard Stanley say, "Who is it?" as he stood up, moving in behind me.

The door swung out slowly and Frank came in the door first. He saw us ready and immediately said, "Everything's all right. We're gonna take the Captain to the front." He stepped past me and went to the bed where the Captain lay. I moved to the door, holding it open with the toe of my boot and looked closer at the four guys standing on the tier. One held a folded green canvas army stretcher. The others just stood there leaning against the railing.

Stepping back, I asked Frank, "What's the deal with those threats we heard on the radio?" Frank looked up from the Captain, made a wry facial expression and said, "No one knows yet," and turned back to the Captain. I stepped back against the opposite wall and watched him and the door. I noticed the knives the four had in their belts as they waited patiently out on the tier. Leaning against the cell wall, I forced myself to relax.

Frank then stepped back saying, "All right. Let's get him out of here but we gotta be careful 'cuz there's still some crazies out there and no one knows who they are." Stanley helped Frank sit the Captain up in the bed and they got under each of his shoulders. I moved over and lifted his legs and we swung him off the bed. Slowly I backed out of the cell with both arms wrapped around the Captain's legs. Frank said to get a blanket and pillow, and Boots followed us out with them.

Once we were standing on the tier with the Captain, two of the strangers had unfolded the stretcher. We lowered him onto it and stood back watching Frank tuck the blanket around and adjust the straps. Finally he stood up. "He's all set," Frank said as the four guys moved over. While they lifted the stretcher I stepped back to the cell door and told Weasel to stay with the other hostage.

After hearing the lock engage on the door, I turned down the tier to where Frank stood at the top of the stairway. Inside the stairwell the stretcher bearers had the Captain tipped up on end to get him around the narrow turn. It took a few tries and a couple times they almost dropped the stretcher. But they got him to the bottom safely and Frank and I ambled on down behind them.

Standing in the water, Frank readjusted the blanket over the Captain, slipped the pillow back where his head was, and announced again that we were set to go. With Stanley and Boots in the lead and Frank walking beside the stretcher, I brought up the rear as we waded out of the cellblock.

Smoke rolled up the hallway from the direction of the gym like a huge bellow— wave after wave of it passed over us. I'd pulled my gas mask over my face as we came out of the cell. I couldn't smell it, but it felt hot against all exposed skin. And as we moved down the right side of the corridor, the heat wafted over us hotter and hotter. Passing through the open security gates between the prison center and living area, the heat became unbearable. Ahead I thought I could see a reddish glow through the smoke and then Frank and the guys on the stretcher turned to the left into the chow hall and the heat subsided.

Moving through the huge, smoke-filled room Frank slowed and as I stepped closer beside him he mumbled, "That fire in the gym is gonna get worse. Already we can't get near it and this is the only route around to the other side." We trudged on into the kitchen and turned to the right into the guard's chow hall. The only light came through the two doors and from a working lightbulb that shined behind the serving line. Crossing the waterlogged carpeting of the cop shop, it was like walking on a big sponge. Then we were back out in the long corridor with the fire at our back.

We waded across the hallway with the wall on our right again. We followed it past the closed chapel door and toward the control center gates. I kept expecting someone to leap out and block our path and I constantly glanced ahead and behind straining to see through the smoke.

Then from ahead I heard a muffled string of words and six shapes appeared out of the smoke. I quickly waded around the Captain and the four guys carrying him, and as Frank and I moved up beside Stanley and Boots, the six masked convicts stepped to the side and waved us on through the control center gates. We continued past the group through the gates and into the short administrative hallway.

The smoke thinned somewhat. It was thickest above our heads, rolling along near the ceiling in the same direction we were going. At the visiting room door, Boots and Stanley strolled right in. Frank and I followed them and the stretcher bearers followed behind us. I saw Felix and four of his crew at the other doorway leading into the lobby. About half a dozen others stood at the wall of windows watching the gym fire. Everyone turned, watching our group bring the Captain in the room.

The four guys carrying the Captain laid him on the long, middle visiting table. Frank went to him and pulled the blanket back, looking intently at his bandaged head. Stanley and I planted ourselves on the end of the table and watched as Felix called different guys over, gave them mumbled instructions, and they hustled away on some directed errand. Other guys came in from the lobby and went to where the Captain laid. They would gaze down at him and walk away. One or two made comments at him, most guys just stared at his swollen, wrapped face and head. I couldn't relax and kept watching both doors, keeping an eye on everyone that came close enough to be a possible threat. I expected a confrontation. Those threats still rang clear in my head.

Felix walked around the end of the table and asked Frank, "Is he ready?" Frank continued tucking the blanket ends under the straps and said, "I can't do anything else for him," and stood glancing back and forth from the Captain's covered feet to his bandaged head. Felix motioned to the four stretcher bearers saying, "Okay, let's get him out of here."

Stanley and I hopped off the table end as the four guys lifted the stretcher and carried him out past us to the lobby. Felix walked ahead and the rest of us followed the stretcher through the lobby as far as the front doors. We stood just inside, watching Felix and the four convicts on the stretcher move down the two steps and into no-man's land toward the front gate.

Felix reached the gate first and he started talking with two suited officials on the other side. He turned, pointed at the Captain on the stretcher, and continued saying something. They were too far away for any of us in the lobby to hear the conversation, but evidently an agreement had been worked out earlier and this was the exchange that had been agreed upon.

Two large boxes are brought forward and laid at the feet of the officials. Felix waved the stretcher forward and the four guys laid the Captain beside the closed gate. Heads nodded on both sides of the gate. Finally, Felix and the four others walked, smiling, back up the sidewalk toward us in the lobby. When Felix came through the lobby doors he said, "It's done!" and turned to watch the gate.

We continued watching as the gate rattled open and four cops in black combat uniforms rushed in, grabbed the stretcher handles and hurried out with it. Another uniformed cop wrestled the two boxes through the open gate and he backed out as the gate squeaked close with a bang. The entire exchange didn't last more than 30 seconds.

I watched them carry the stretcher around the little building just outside the gate and toward the parking lot. I heard the ambulance scream away as the gate was closing. I wondered if that Captain knows he's on his way to a hospital. I doubt that he even knows he exists.

The four guys who'd carried the stretcher left the lobby again toward the gate. They retrieved the two large cardboard boxes and hauled them back into the lobby. As soon as they set them down, they tore into them. I kept watching the officials at the front gate as the melee started and ended over sacks of ham sandwiches and cookies wrapped in cellophane. The same suited officials stood just outside the gate watching the lobby entrance intently, as if they were expecting something more to happen or more hostages to appear.

16   The Negotiations

Backing away from the lobby door and the view of the officials and forces at the front, I turned and made my way around small groups munching the goodies from the boxes. Frank, Felix, and Lucky stood near the visiting room door. Stepping over beside Frank, Lucky said, "We've got to give up three more guards to be able to talk with those TV people." He counted points off on his fingers of their next move. It had already been determined that Felix would speak to the media. He said, "I need someone out there with me to witness this." Lucky quickly said, "We'll get someone out there with you. We also gotta be sure this is on TV."

Then, from the visiting room, a group brought in two partially clothed, blind-folded, tied hostages. Felix told the group to take them and hold them in the lobby. Another hostage is carried in on a stretcher and he too is taken toward the lobby. Felix and Lucky followed, talking about the main points he would bring out in the forthcoming interview.

Frank and I hesitated, then we saw Stanley and Boots at the far side of the lobby and strolled over to them. Closer to the front, the three hostages were held surrounded by eight or ten guys. Stanley asked in between bites of his sandwich, "What's going on? What are they doing?" Frank stared at the scene in front of us and said, "They're gonna go out and talk to the news media." We stood watching as Felix and Lucky selected the witnesses that would accompany Felix to the gate and they made their way to the front doors. We moved closer to the left side of the doors as Lucky told the three convicts walking out, "I'll let you know if it's for real. One of you guys keep watch and I'll give you the cut sign if this isn't on TV." They nodded their heads and passed through the doors toward the gate.

We watched as Felix reached the gate and saw the officials shake their heads on the other side. The news cameraman stood beside the two suits holding his camera pointed at the ground. Words were exchanged, or at least it looked like they were talking. Then Felix backed away, turned and he and the two with him stalked back up the sidewalk toward us in the lobby. "What the hell's going on . . ." Lucky mumbled beside us.

When Felix walked through the doors he snarled, "They want the three hostages released before they'll let me talk to the media." It got suddenly quiet in the lobby. Then someone behind us said, "Those are trained negotiators and they won't give nothing without getting as much as they can first." A low murmur started around the lobby and Felix pointed to the hostages. "Take off those blindfolds and let 'em go." The guys standing around the guards moved to take off their rags, and pushed them toward the lobby doors. Their hands were still tied and they ambled barefoot down the two steps to the sidewalk, then they broke into a shuffling run toward the gate.

Armed State Police rushed to the outside of the gate as the two newly released hostages reached it. From a distance it looked like they weren't sure on the outside that the two were guards. But finally the gate came open and they were allowed to walk through. They were immediately surrounded and escorted around the little building at gunpoint.

The guard on the stretcher was carried out through the lobby doors. I didn't recognize him but it was obvious that his leg was broken, seeing the way it is bent. He shifted around on the stretcher, wincing in pain at each jarring step. The four guys set the stretcher down beside the gate and started back toward the lobby. They'd taken just a few steps when they hesitated and turned toward the suited officials. Something was said from one of the officials and then they continued up the sidewalk again.

When the guys reached the lobby, one of them announced, "The cops said they're ready for the interview." Everyone turned to continue watching the front gate. The cameraman came forward, pointing his shoulder-mounted camera at the guard being hauled out on the stretcher. As the gate slammed shut, he swung the camera up, pointing it at the lobby entrance.

Lucky said, "It looks like they're ready for you." Felix stepped to the door saying, "You have someone go check to see that this is live . . ." and he and his two companions moved down the steps and onto the sidewalk again. The rest of us stood in place at the lobby doors and watched the negotiations resume.

As Felix started talking into the camera, Lucky waved me over to the side and said, "I want you to go to the cellblock and check the TV to be sure this interview . . ." he waved a hand toward the front, "is on live." I nodded, "Sure—I'll go," I said. Frank and Stanley stepped over to listen and Lucky said, "It'll probably be on Channel 7 'cuz that's the number painted on the side of the camera out there." I slowly nodded and he continued, "Give it a few minutes and check the other channels too before you start back. But mainly, we gotta know that it's being broadcast live." I told him that I understood the importance and I glanced at Stanley. He immediately said he'd come with me and we moved back through the lobby.

On into the visiting room, we stopped and pulled our gas masks over our faces. Continuing on we passed through the short hallway with the fried offices on each side. Into the swamp again, we made our way through the control center gates and past the group watching the entrance. Out into the long hallway, we briskly waded to the guards' chow hall, into the kitchen, and out into the smoke-filled main chow hall.

We had to grope our way from table to table that were bolted to the floor. I could hear the roar of the fire through the two walls that separated us from it. Then back into the long hallway and swirling hot smoke and flying red ash. It was as if the corridor had turned into a huge flue. I could feel the heat blowing from the gym and we broke into a lope up the hall to the cellblock.

Wading to the steps I couldn't help but notice that the cellblock was socked full of blue-gray smoke. I thought about how Weasel and the hostage were making it and bounded up the steps to the second tier. Feeling our way from cell to cell, we reached ours and pounded on the door. I had to pull my mask up so Weasel could recognize my face pressed against the glass. When I heard the lock snap, I jerked the door open and Stanley and I rushed in and pulled the door shut as quickly as we could to prevent smoke from coming into the cell.

Both Weasel and Diego had towels around their faces. The cell was already filling with smoke and smoke was blowing in through the two vents on the cell wall. The guard stood on the end of the bed reaching up and stuffing strips of sheet into the small square holes of the vent. He said, "The smoke started coming in through the ducts about 10 minutes ago." Weasel had a handful of strips and he hopped up on the sink to continue stuffing the vent above. He said, "What's going on out front? We haven't heard anything but more threats on the radio." Stanley answered with, "Some of the hostages have been freed. The talks started again at the gate." I moved to the back of the cell and noticed smoke pouring out through the open window. These two guys were doing all right. At least they weren't sitting—choking on smoke and doing nothing about it. Yeah, these guys will be all right. I stepped back to the door and nonchalantly said, "We'll be back in a little while," looking up at Diego still stuffing cloth into the vent holes. "We're working on getting you out too," I said to him. He just looked at me, not saying anything. With that I turned and pushed the door open and Stanley followed me out on the tier.

We moved down the tier to the TV room. The door stood open and we walked in, not bothering to close it. The room was full of smoke but we wouldn't be there that long and we had our gas masks. Stanley moved over to the front picnic table and turned on the TV. I looked out the side window at the gym fire next door and shook my head, remembering the contents. Then I stepped to the TV screen and focused on it.

A newsman stood in the middle of the prison parking lot with a microphone in his hand. In the background behind him the gym fire filled most of the screen with the smoke rolling skyward, making it look as if the whole prison was burning. I reached out and turned the volume knob and the newsman's voice said, "Not known yet how many are left inside, but we'll let you know as they are released." A ribbon of block letters ran across the bottom of the screen: SPECIAL NEWS REPORT FROM THE SANTA FE PRISON RIOT. The camera panned across the front of the prison showing the National Guard and their equipment. The newsman kept talking, giving a blow-by-blow recap of the last two days. I reached out and flipped the channel selector to Channel 7. It was a different view of the prison from another angle in the parking lot, but nothing showing or mentioning the ongoing interview at the front gate. This channel just showed the backs of the crowd of spectators and troops standing at the fence looking inward at the prison. The voice mentioned a state of emergency had been called by the Governor and police forces had been arriving at the prison from all over the state. I flipped the channel selector again and it stopped on a religious program, flipped it again and it landed on a western movie. I kept turning the dial around to the first channel again. The newsman on this channel was still giving a history of what had happened already. I flipped it to Channel 7 again and it was the same thing as before. Stanley said, "Leave it there a couple of minutes. Maybe they aren't hooked in yet." That sounded logical and we stood watching the screen for about four or five minutes. The channel kept showing the scene from the distance of the parking lot. The voice mentioned how many hostages had been released but that the prison spokesman wouldn't say how many were left inside. Still nothing had been said about the live interview. I flipped the channel again. Every channel had the same thing as before. I stopped the selector on each broadcasting channel and still nothing. "We've been here about 12 minutes now," I said. Stanley moved up and turned the channel selector to Channel 7 again and said, "If it was coming on, it would be on that channel but they're not putting it on the air." We'd been gone from the front about 20 minutes. "They're not gonna show it," I said and glanced at Stanley. He said, "We've given it plenty of time if they were." I stepped back from the screen. "Come on," I said. "We've given it time," and we both turned, leaving the TV on, we shuffled out the door and down the tier toward the front of the cellblock.

We didn't stop at the cell. We kept going to the stairs and back through the labyrinth of turns and rooms to the front. On the way I tried to make some sense out of our discovery. Why would the officials go to such lengths to have a news camera? They didn't know we would check? I had more questions than answers. One thing was for sure, they lied about allowing Felix to talk on live TV about the prison conditions. But why hide what the public should know? With Stanley in the lead, we felt our way along past the fire and through the kitchen. Out again, passing the guys guarding the control center gates—they just waved us on with no words exchanged.

In reaching the lobby, most everyone there was crowded around the entrance watching the front gate through the doors. I moved around and past the guys until I spotted Lucky and Frank at the front of the herd. They were watching Felix still speaking into the camera on the other side of the gate. As soon as I stepped up beside Frank I said, "None of that's on the TV." Both Frank and Lucky glanced at me with surprised double takes, looking at me, at the gate and back at me. I said, "Check it out," pointing past the fence and crowd. "See that van over there by those National Guard trucks? That's one news crew and there's one more out there somewhere and they're the only ones broadcasting live on the television. I stepped over the other side of the door frame to locate the other news crew. From the angle of the camera shots on the TV, it had to be on the far left of the prison parking lot. But there were too many vehicles and too many people moving around to find it. I turned back to Lucky. "None of the stations mentioned the interview or even pointed their cameras in the direction of the gate." He looked past me at the phony interview. "How about Channel 7? What was on there?" he asked in a low voice. "There's only two channels reporting on the riot and Channel 7 has a crew out there somewhere," I said pointing to the left of the prison. "They're talking about the riot and the hostages freed, but nothing about that," I said pointing at Felix and the people at the gate. Lucky kept nodding his head at everything said. Then he stepped deliberately past me and pushed through the lobby door to the landing beyond. He brought his hand to his mouth and made a short shrill whistling sound between his fingers.

Everyone at the gate—Felix, his two convict witnesses, the officials and the camera man—turned at hearing the piercing noise and saw Lucky making a cutting motion across his throat. Felix turned back to the officials, said something to them, turned away, and quickly walked up the sidewalk toward us in the lobby.

I stood beside Frank at the doors watching the group leave the gate. As Felix came through the doors he said, "Was it on the television?" I started to explain again what I'd seen, but Lucky spoke up first. "They're probably just recording all of what you said and they'll probably cut out what they don't want the public to know 'cuz none of it has been broadcast live." Someone else piped in with, "They'll just use what you said against you." Then there were four or five other shouts of anger around the lobby as others realized the deception. Two groups started arguing further back in the crowd. One group wanted to keep the talks going to end the madness. Others shouted their opinion that we shouldn't be talking at all—just throwing bodies out. I watched Felix and Lucky. They moved through the crowded lobby and seemed to be acknowledging the raving anger build. I realized how tenuous and fragile all sanity hung in the balance at that moment. I glanced at Frank beside me—the expression on his face was unreadable. But something wasn't quite right, as if the deception was expected and planned on. I asked him, "What's the hell's going on man? What are they doing?" indicating Felix and Lucky as they left the lobby for the center of the prison. He looked at me and said, "They're gonna send out one more hostage. It's gonna be a message." I stared at his face to read what that meant. It sounded ominous, but before I could ask "what message," he brushed past saying, "Come on," and I followed him through the lobby toward the prison center. Stanley and Boots fell in behind us.

Frank led the way into the visiting room and took us to the wall of windows facing out at the gym fire. We stood watching as the fire seemed to be gaining intensity. Flames could be seen coming out between the top of the side wall and roof at the eaves. From where we stood we could see the entire right side wall of the gym. Then a rumbling noise started that reverberated all through the joint. Sparks and flames shot skyward and the roof of the gym crashed in on the floor. It happened all at once, black smoke belched out the huge side wall windows, exploding outward with glass and bits of burning pieces that showered the nearby grass and into patches of snow that hadn't yet melted. I ducked my head at the initial implosion and explosion. But I had to watch, captivated by an enormous cloud of debris shooting up and out like a bomb exploding . . . then it rained down on the surrounding rooftops of the prison. Some of the stuff rattled off the outside windows and bars of the visiting room. "Hot-damn!!" I mumbled with my tongue tied and glanced at Stanley on my left. He stood staring at the fire too. I turned to Frank on my right and he stood looking over my shoulder at the visiting room door behind me.

I spun around and there stood Bear and Lucky talking in Spanish with Felix at the door. Two other guys stood holding the tied arms of a naked guard. I assumed he's a guard because I didn't recognize him at first. Looking closer, his hands were cuffed with steel bracelets at his back. A rag of some sort hung from his mouth down his chin. It had been stuffed in his mouth so full that it forced his jaw down, distorting his whole face. Then I noticed the orange-red hair and remembered him. Yeah, he's a guard all right. I remembered him when I had to work in the kitchen and he was the on-duty guard there. I remember . . . he was given the name "Grits" by convict workers. A name he wouldn't answer to but a name that fit him nevertheless. He'd carry a spoon around the kitchen and sample out of all the prepared pans for the next meal. When he wasn't eating something, he'd sit in the office and scheme on the convict workers. He took perverse pleasure in harassing "his boys" as he called us kitchen workers. Evidently he'd been transferred out of the kitchen to the graveyard shift. And there he stood in all his glory. He wasn't blindfolded and rolled his head around trying to see what was coming. You could see the fear in his eyes, as if he knew he was a trapped meal—soon to be served.

We four stood in place with our backs to the windows, the fire outside forgotten. The drama was unfolding before us and all it took was the stomach to watch.

Grits was pulled in between two long tables and three more guys appeared at the door and went to him. Bear left through the same door and Lucky and Felix continued talking for a moment. Then Lucky stepped over to the table and said something to the guys holding the naked guard. He was instantly lifted off his feet and slammed face first onto the long visiting table.

Still I couldn't figure what this was all about. Glancing at Frank I whispered, "What's going on man?" He didn't look at me, just said breathless, "WATCH," and I turned back.

The five guys leaned down over the guard, holding him pressed into the tabletop. They kept glancing around expectantly at Felix and Lucky who stood by the hallway door, talking in low monotones. Then Bear appeared in the doorway and handed Lucky a long-handled push broom. All three exchanged a few indistinct words in Spanish, and Felix said, "Do it," in English. Lucky paced around the end of the table, moving down its length. He stopped and bent down at the guard's head, whispered something in his hear and stood up twisting the broom end off the stick.

At that moment I realized, or I felt I knew, what was coming. I felt like a rock skipping across the surface of a pond and looking back at the person that threw me.

Lucky dropped the broom head on the floor and kicked it away. He said something in Spanish and the two guys on Grits' legs pulled them apart into a spread eagle and wrenched his bare feet around the table edge. He must have known what was coming and tried to kick free, but they just twisted his feet and legs further around under the tabletop.

This is the message that's gonna be sent special to the gate. This is the message that Frank referred to.

Lucky strolled down the left side of the guard, twirling the broom handle like a baton. He said something again to the guys holding the bucking, twisting guard, and they slumped down across his body and held him fast for the moment that Lucky drove the stick, two-handed, plunging it down between the spread legs. Grits made a feeble attempt to scream into the rag—it sounded like mewing.

Frank let out a low moan beside me. I felt muscles tighten in every part of my being and the peaking madness seemed to be looking back at me.

The guard twisted his head around as if he was trying to see what Lucky was doing. He kept pushing the stick in deeper and deeper. Then a squirt of blood sprayed out and Lucky and the two holding the splayed legs leaped away and Grits started beating his feet against the tabletop. The implanted stick wobbled back and forth.

Lucky stood wiping his hands up and down on his pant legs and said something to the guys still holding Grits to the table. They lifted him kicking off the tabletop and set him standing on the floor where he stood frozen, bent over at the waist to take the pressure off the implanted stick.

He stood stock-still for the longest time. You could see the blood running down the handle to drip, then pour, off the end onto the floor behind him. Lucky motioned for the three guys behind the guard to move back. Then he stepped to the guard and said, "Walk!" But Grits just stood there trembling, his whole body shaking, bent over. Lucky shouted at him, "Walk you maggot mother fucker . . ." and swung, slapping the guard on the side of the head. Grits stumbled sideways into the table and tentatively tried to rise up straight. Lucky moved in on him, grabbing him by the throat and hoisted him up. He said, "The only way you're getting out of here is to walk out," and released his grip. The guard took a hesitant step, raising up a little straighter. He still made a kind of eerie mewing sound but it sounded more guttural—like a growl. He stepped forward a couple of steps, rising up on his toes to take the pressure off the stick. He continued ahead toward Lucky, stepping backwards between the long tables and on around the end toward the visitor's exit and out toward the lobby.

We followed Felix and Bear and the trail of blood out of the visiting room. Then ahead of us, the shouts of laughter and cat calls from the lobby as the impaled guard passed through. We continued around the corner into the lobby and saw the guard stumble down the two steps to the sidewalk outside.

Then the roar of shouted anger started outside. It got louder and louder as the naked guard tried to walk on his toes in an animated shuffle that had to be unbearably painful from the stick that raked the concrete behind him.

We stood in the darkened shadows at the back of the lobby, listening at the building roar of angry shouts outside. The lobby doors were blocked from our view by the crowd of convicts watching Grits walk the distance down the sidewalk to the front gate. Frank mumbled something beside me and it sounded like, "We're in big time trouble now . . ."

17 Realities of Fear

The shouting and screaming from outside subsided a little. A few distant voices could still be heard. Someone out there demanded the State Police-National Guard take action. "Do something," the voice bellowed. "What are you afraid of . . . why don't you storm the prison . . . shoot 'em all . . . kill 'em . . kill 'em!" The words heard in the lobby were chilling. Everyone inside listened in rapt attention. A new wave of fear passed through me. I imagined the forces outside gearing up at that moment to rush in to save the rest of the guards. They now had their justification and I could feel what was imminent.

Then someone in front of me laughed and shouted, "Let's set one on fire. Let him run to the gate and see what they say about that." Others around the lobby started laughing at the idea, but I knew some of these guys were serious about it. All that was needed now was someone to co-sign the idea and it would happen. Most of the convicts in this room had nothing to lose, or felt they had nothing. Being confined outcasts of society gave everyone in the room at that moment a tangible goal and power. For some, it was a determination to force our keepers to deal with us honestly. For others, it was just entertainment and opportunity to inflict agony and terror for the moment and to hell with the consequences. More and more I could feel the second group was just a hair's breath from getting us all killed. Other ideas were shouted out with a building exuberance around the crowded lobby and Felix, Lucky, Bear, and others in that crew stepped into the center of the floor.

Felix told everyone, "Shut the fuck up!!" and he pointed to individuals around the room telling them the same thing. The room got suddenly quiet again. He glared around the room at the head runners and said, "No one does anything to the hostages unless I say so." Everyone stayed silent and he continued, "We're gonna see what they do out front about the negotiations. Anyone that has hostages, go to 'em. Stay with 'em and don't hurt 'em." Very menacingly he growled, "And if any of you motor mouths don't like it, I'm right here," and he slapped his hand against his chest. Still, no one said anything and no one moved. Then he and his whole crew stalked out in the direction of the prison center.

I let out the breath I was unconsciously holding, when Frank said, "I'll catch up with you guys later," and as Felix passed us, he fell in step beside him. I glanced around the room and saw Stanley with Boots by the overturned pop machine. Strolling over to them I said, "Let's get out of here." Others were leaving the lobby in groups of three and four. We moved through the visiting room and toward the control center. I could hear voices of others in front and behind heading in the same direction.

As we passed through the control gates and started down the long hallway, Frank materialized out of the swirling smoke saying, "I knew it was you guys 'cuz I heard your shoe flapping." He chucked and waded in behind Stanley and me heading for guard's mess hall. The kitchen and two chow halls were now the regular routes around the gym fire. In the main dining room Stanley took the lead and we filed in line behind him. Half listening to Frank behind me, I concentrated on navigating through thick, smothering smoke and Stanley's back. Frank said something about Felix finding out who was making those threats on the radio. Strangely I could hear him and not the roar of the gym fire. Since the roof had fallen in on the gym floor, the fire didn't sound as intense but this smoke was even worse. Stanley guided us around the tables and obstacles laying in the swamp and we made it to the corridor again.

Wading toward the cellblock, the smoke thinned quite a bit. It blew over our heads going in the opposite direction. There must be a draft pulling air and smoke to the gym fire. Amazingly, when we reached Cellhouse 1, it was clear of smoke and I pulled my gas mask off. I didn't know how long this would last, but it was a bit of relief, for a change.

As soon as we reached the cell, Weasel was anxious for answers to his many questions. Frank went into his doctor mode and started checking the crusty burns on the guard and questioning him about how he felt. Weasel kept asking what was going on out front. I didn't want to talk in front of the hostage, so after I used the tape again to repair my shoe, I waved everyone out on the tier. We left Frank smearing salve on the guard's burns and the rest of us went to the TV room.

Once there I explained to Weasel that the officials had lied about the exchange of hostages for the television interview. I told him about the last guard sent out with the stick and the special message he took to the gate.

We sat on the bench watching the TV. The commentator mentioned the recent hostage released. The scene on the TV screen was of the front gate and the forces gathering around the little building outside the gate. We discussed the possibilities of what the officials would do next. Weasel asked about the threats he'd heard over the radio and Boots said he'd heard Felix say that he'd deal with it. I asked Weasel how the guard was and Weasel just shrugged his shoulders and said, "He doesn't believe he'll be released." I nodded my head, not saying anything.

Stanley got our attention by angrily saying, "What the fuck are we supposed to do now?" He stood up by the windows watching the gym fire next door. When I said, "All we can do now is wait," he blew off a disdainful, "Phew!" and turned back to watching out in the cellblock. "The damn smoke is coming back in again," he said and looked at me as if this is all my fault. I knew what was on his mind, or I thought

I did. None of us really knows what's coming next. With that last hostage sent out impaled and Felix off searching for the idiots making those threats, it all felt like something was about to happen that we couldn't control. Everything seemed to be heading for a climax of doom. I felt it but I didn't want to say anything about it and tried to keep the conversation on the facts with a positive outcome. It seemed to me that if we talked about the worst happening, that would just give the worst credibility to becoming real. While Boots and Weasel watched the TV screen, I stood up and moved over to Stanley by the window.

When I stood up, I could see the smoke pouring into the cellblock from the hallway. It wouldn't be long until it filled the block again.

At the window I saw black smoke and sparks rolling skyward as parts of the remaining gym roof continued to collapse in on the floor. All the glass in the huge gym windows was gone on this side of the gym wall. From where we stood we could see down through the bars to the gym floor. The fire looked like it had a life of its own and it looked like it was regenerating itself.

I glanced at Stanley beside me and said, "What's the deal brother? You know as well . . ." He wouldn't look at me and stalked away to the table and sat down between Boots and Weasel on the bench. I turned and looked at him startled and angry. "What the fuck is your problem?" I mumbled.

As he sat down he said, "We've got to leave that fuckin' hostage on his own. We can't stay with him anymore." He pounded his fist on the bench with every word. "We gotta find another place to hide until all this bullshit is over." Weasel and Boots had turned sideways in their seats watching him. I stood by the window looking at him with astonishment, listening to his breathless rush of words, waiting for him to finish. He kept on, "None of this hostage watching has been my idea. I didn't like it from the beginning and I don't like it now. We can't help him, we can't, we can't . . ." He suddenly stopped talking and looked at each of us for a response. Weasel and Boots didn't say anything. They just glanced away, dumbfounded at the outburst. I couldn't let it hang and had to say something. "Man, you know we can't leave the hostage on his own, not now. We've committed ourselves to this side and if we try to run out, we'll be treated just like those we hauled to the gym." I waved my arm at the fire behind me and we glared at each other across the space between us. Surely he knew what he was suggesting. If we were to attempt to bail out now, we'd just get ourselves killed. In prison a person can't get away with committing to one side, be involved in what we had already seen and done, and then try to run out. He scowled at me as if I should co-sign his ludicrous rambling—as if I'm being unloyal to our friendship by my not agreeing with him. I can't scoff his words, no matter how ridiculous they sound. I tried to mellow the glower on my face and said, "Brother, I don't like this shit any more than you do . . . none of us do." I pointed at Boots and Stanley, "But man, we're committed to see this through. Let me get Frank and let's see what he says." I held my hands up. "Just stay right there. I'll go get Frank," and I moved toward the door.

As I walked out of the room, I couldn't help but notice the clouds of smoke rolling in the block. It had already filled the front half of the cellblock and moved toward the TV room.

I ambled down the tier with thoughts flashing on Stanley. I'd known him since I stepped off the bus three years ago, when I'd arrived here. He worked in the reception building for new prisoners that came in the joint. From day one we'd become friends and partners. I thought I knew him pretty well. I'd never seen him run from trouble or ever thought he would. It's way out of character for him to suggest it. No—no, not now. And even though I'm not sure we're gonna come out on top with the road I've committed us to, we can't run now. I couldn't bring myself to agree with him on running. At the same time, he's my partner and I gotta give him all the room that I can—but still, I don't want to see him end up like John.

When I reached the cell door I walked right in, hesitated for a moment and then asked, "Anything on the radio?" Frank looked up from the bed beside the guard, wrapping his arms, and just shook his head no. I moved to the desk, adjusted the volume and squelch knobs on the radio that sat in the battery charger. It worked all right and I slowly sauntered back to the door. I hadn't thought out what I'd say to Frank and I didn't want to talk in front of Diego. He was paranoid already and I didn't want to frighten him any more than he already was. I said to the guard, "We're gonna have to leave you for a minute." Then I said to Frank, "Come out here and see this man. You gotta check this out." I pushed on the door and went out on the tier to wait against the railing.

Smoke had already filled the block past the cell door and I stood outside waiting and watching it sock us in again. Frank walked out behind me and he said, "Did you know he was in the Tet offensive (in South Vietnam) in '68?" He pointed over his shoulder at the cell with the guard, Diego, still inside. "Yeah, I know," I said. "He was in 'Nam in '68 and '69." Frank leaned on the railing beside me and said, "What's the deal? What did you want to show me? Man, this smoke is bad." He coughed, and pulled his towel over his nose and mouth. "Come on, we gotta talk in the TV room," I said and headed down the tier. He followed and we walked out of the wall of moving smoke that had filled two-thirds of the cellblock. I hadn't bothered to pull my gas mask on yet and we walked into the TV room together. I went to the television and turned the volume down. Frank plopped down on the bench beside Boots.

I stood beside the television, glanced at Stanley, Weasel, and Boots. Then I spoke to Frank. "Some of us think that things have gotten way out of control." I looked at Frank for some kind of reaction—but he just stared at me over his towel wrap and I continued. "We all know what Felix and his crew are trying to get done, but what if it doesn't work? What next? I'm not ready to sacrifice myself for this fuckin' joint." Frank gave no indication that my words made the slightest impression on him. Stanley started to say something and I looked over at him, but Frank interrupted by saying, "It's not gonna come to that. Those suit-wearing officials aren't gonna let the negotiations fail, not on their part. They won't let things get any more out of control than they already are." He pointed to the television screen and went on. "There's too much media coverage out there. Oh, if we were behind a wall where they could be hidden from view, we'd be in big trouble. But with those fences out there, they can't be sure that they aren't being seen by those television cameras." He pulled his towel off and kept talking without missing a beat. "So far no hostages have been killed, so the Governor can't risk his political career on sending in troops and getting a lot more people killed. So far, all the killings have been done by us. Yeah, and they probably know about the bodies in the gym. But they don't care about us. And they actually don't care what happens to these guards 'cuz the guards are just cannon fodder for the state. But you can bet the Governor is keeping track of what goes on here and his concern isn't this fuckin' place. His concern is his political future. You'll see. Those officials at the gate will agree to anything Felix says now. They'll probably let him talk live on the TV. They'll stand out there at the gate and look reasonable and accommodating for the media. But in the end, they'll lie and smile and just cover their asses." His last words trailed off and left images in my mind of peaceful settlement and agreements to change and everything will be fine and we'll all be alive tomorrow.

Then Stanley said, "I still think we should hide until the National Guard comes in." He sat on the bench looking as if we should agree with him. The expression on his face said he'd already made up his mind about all this. I looked at him and at Weasel next to him. Then Frank asked matter-of-factly, "Where can you hide? Tell me and I'll go with you. Where can we hide in here?" He leaned forward and looked at Stanley. "Come on man. Get real . . . you know we couldn't get away with running out now. If anyone runs out now, they'll be considered a rat and end up with the rest of the rats." No one said anything for a long few seconds. I glanced at Stanley, then at Frank, waiting for one or the other to say something to relieve the tension. Stanley sat there fumbling with his gas mask, looking at the floor. Finally I said, "What you said about the media makes sense and there's no place anyone can hide in here." Frank nodded his head and I glanced over at Stanley and he slowly raised up looking at me. He didn't say anything but I could see the haunted eyes that said he was unconvinced about anything Frank said. And now I'd have to worry about him slipping off somewhere and trying to hide and probably getting himself killed in the process.

Frank pointed at the television and said, "Turn it up. Let's hear what they're doing." I reached for the volume control and stepped over to sit next to Stanley on the bench.

The smoke had drifted in the room but it was insignificant to what showed on the TV screen. Everyone sat glued to the unfolding drama.

The scene was of the front of the joint, the sidewalk and doors of the lobby entrance, the fancy lettering above the entrance naming the asylum, and movement inside, but it was too dark to make anyone out distinctly. Then Felix and Lucky appeared at the doors. They shuffled down the two steps, hesitated, and strided down the sidewalk toward the camera. It refocused and the commentator's voice said, "We'll switch live to the negotiations at the front of the prison now."

This is what we should have seen an hour ago. This scene on TV probably would have saved that last guard from being impaled.

I was riveted to the TV screen, but it kept blurring and my ears popped as if I was on an airplane. The figures on the screen were talking, but I couldn't hear what they were saying. I turned my head, looking around the TV room, and everything looked surreal. The television, the walls, the table kept blurring and refocusing and blurring again. I shook my head hard trying to clear it, but that didn't help. Suddenly

I thought about the smoke. There's something in the smoke, something I'm breathing. I groped for the gas mask on top of my head, pulled it down over my face and blew out to clear it. Then I took a couple of slow, deep breaths but that didn't help either. Everything around the edge of my vision fogged over and I croaked, "Ahhh fuck . . ." and leaped to my feet. I glanced around and everything still looked unfocused and blurred. I glanced down at Stanley and he was watching me with a puzzled expression. I lightly pushed off away from the table and stumbled backwards into the wall. My head spun and I bent over groaning and my stomach flipped. I saw sparks burst white and tasted something foul that filled my mouth and just got my mask off in time to spew a yellowish brown liquid that splashed on the floor at my feet. I groaned again and, amazingly, my head cleared and I felt better. Actually I felt clammy. Hot—but better. I raised up slowly, wiping my mouth on my left sleeve and Stanley and Frank were in front of me. They were both looking at me as if I was a patient. Stanley spoke first. "Are you all right man?" I looked at him and attempted a smile and said, "I don't, shit, I don't know," and turned my head to spit more of the nasty taste from my mouth. Then before I could move, Stanley had my left arm and Frank grabbed my right and they pulled and directed me to the bench. I told them that I was okay, and I actually did feel all right. My vision had cleared and my stomach quieted. My legs felt a little shaky and I could still taste whatever I spit on the floor but no matter, Frank had me as his patient now. He said down beside me and took my left arm, pressing his fingers into my wrist. I glanced up to see Stanley and Weasel looking at me as if I was dying or something.

I told Frank again, "I'm all right . . ." and tried to pull my arm away from him. He just held it tighter saying, "Wait a minute." So I sat back down and let him get a full measure of my pulse. Finally he released my arm and announced my heartbeat normal. I started to stand and said, "I need some water," but before I could raise off the bench, Frank pulled me back down. Weasel looked on and said, "I'll get some water," and he took off at a trot out of the TV room. I had a sudden flash of anger because it was irritating to be treated like an invalid. But then I just smiled at my friends around me and sat back. Frank asked in his gravel voice, "When's the last time you ate something?" I opened my mouth to say, but I really couldn't remember when I had eaten last. Stanley piped in with, "We ate some Fritos two days ago." I looked up at him and nodded my head, remembering that we had eaten some of those chips from that pile of stolen items. Then Weasel was back and handed me a tumbler of water that I immediately drafted down. Frank and Stanley continued their discussion of my strange behavior as if I wasn't there. I smiled at Weasel, and Frank turned and pointed a serious finger at my chest. With all the authority of his medical opinion, he announced that I'd had an anxiety attack. He said, "With all this madness going on, and in combination with not eating anything for so long, you had an attack of nerves." And he was serious. I took a dubious sip from the cup of water and said, "Come on man . . . the next thing you'll be telling me is I'm pregnant and this was just morning sickness." I glanced over at Stanley, wanting him to confirm my assessment of Frank's quackery. He and Weasel were talking in low tones, looking at me suspiciously. I heard Stanley say, "Don't let him out of your sight." He was telling Weasel to watch me and I had to grin at them. They were actually concerned.

I could see it in their faces but that wasn't necessary. I said to Weasel, "Yeah, you better keep a close eye on me," and I lunged to the left and passed Frank and bounded to the TV room door before they could react. As I walked out I heard Frank say, "This is serious shit, Banker*—you shouldn't . . ." and I was around the end of the tier before I looked back and saw Weasel walking out the door after me.

I continued down the tier to the cell. At the door I stopped and turned on him, "Man, you ain't gotta watch me or follow me. I'm all right!" He just walked up to me, not saying anything. The smug expression on his face told me that he was given a mission by Stanley and nothing I said made a bit of difference.

When I pulled on the door to go inside, I saw the guard spin around from watching something out the back cell window. I moved on in the cell and said to him, "What's out there man?" He pointed out the window saying, "There's another fire next door." I stepped past him to the desk and saw fires in the Dorm A-2 next door. It looked like it had just been started 'cuz there wasn't any smoke coming out the windows yet. Then as I watched, another fire flared up and I could see some guys scurry away from it. "Hey, check it out," I said. "The crazy bastards are starting more fires." Behind me Weasel peered out over my shoulder. "Do you think they'll set everything on fire?" he asked with concern. I nodded my head and said, "Yeah, they'll probably try . . . but we don't have to worry 'cuz there's nothing that'll burn in the cellblocks." I kept watching the guys next door move through the dorm with their bottles of dry-cleaning fluid. I hoped they couldn't set the cellblocks on fire, but with that fluid . . . anything was possible. And with enough determination, this whole joint could be burned to a blackened husk.

18   The Trip Out

After refilling the tumbler with water, I stood behind Weasel and the guard watching the fire gain strength as it moved through the dorm. It looked like there was probably a group effort in setting the fires. Yeah, it would be the next logical move to make—burn as much of the prison as possible before giving up. We now had fires going on both sides of us and there was no telling what'd be burned next.

Just then the radio made a loud garbled squawk on the desk. It made us jump with a start and we stood in the middle of the floor staring at it when it squawked again and a voice said, "Bring all the hostages to the tap room." I recognized Lucky's voice with his unique clipped English. He said, "Bring all guards to the tap room." No one moved. We just kept eyeing the radio as if it were alive. Nothing else was said from it and Weasel said, "Was that for real?" and turned looking at me dig the tattered pieces of paper out of my pocket—it had the coded locations written on it. "Yeah, I think it's for real. That was Lucky on the radio," I said.

Setting the cup on the sink, I started running my finger down the two lines of places written. One line had the actual location and next to it was the coded name. As I moved my finger I thought out loud saying, "Tap room, tap room. Where the fuck are you . . ." There it is, second from the bottom. "Yeah, it's for real," I said, looking up at Weasel. "It's the visiting room," and glanced at the guard saying, "Are you ready to get out of this . . . this mad house?" He watched me but I couldn't read anything on his face. It was covered in some kind of silver-white cream—compliments of Frank. He just stood there transfixed, not saying anything. Then he said, "Are you guys really going to let me go?" It surprised me because I thought he'd be elated that he was finally getting out. There would be no other reason for wanting all the hostages brought to the visiting room. I said to him, "No man, we're not letting you go. We're gonna take you to the front . . . this is for real." He just stared at me, not saying anything. I turned to Weasel and said, "Go tell the guys what's going on." He rushed out of the cell leaving Diego, the hostage guard, and me alone.

As soon as the door shut I said, "I believe you're going out on this trip. Most everyone wants this shit to end. It's gone on long enough." He hung his head, looking at the floor. I stepped over directly in front of him and said, "It's gonna be all right," placing my left hand on his upper arm and immediately felt the trembling cruise through his body. "Just stay close to us and we'll walk you out, no sweat." The fear was getting the best of him. He knew about the different factions vying for control. He knew about the threats on the radio and he knew his vulnerability. "It's gonna be all right," I said. "Remember those times in 'Nam when you were scared shitless." All combat vets know this feeling. "When you weren't sure that you'd make it . . . hell man, think about it. You came through that all right and you came home." He looked up at me, staring into my eyes. He had to see the fear in mine because I could see it in his. He started to say something but at that moment the door flew open and in streamed Stanley, Frank, Boots, and Weasel. They were all talking at once.

"It's true," I said. "We're to take him to the visiting room. That's all that was said." They each had that excited, hopeful, but weary anticipation surge expressingly across their faces. Stanley literally hopped from foot to foot. Frank being all business said, "We're gonna need to wrap our faces in wet towels. That fire's roaring again." I could hear the distinct low rumbling moan that sounded like thunder in the distance. Weasel and Boots rushed in circles gathering towels and stuffing them under running water in the sink. There was no wasted motion as everyone prepared to leave the cell again.

Frank helped the guard wrap a wet towel around his face and head, leaving only his eyes uncovered. He told him that the bandages would give him protection on his arms and hands. I wrapped my towel over my head and the back of my neck, knowing the gas mask wouldn't cover these places from the heat and flying ash. I helped Weasel and Boots get their wet wraps in place over all exposed skin. I attempted to help Stanley, but he became sullen and morose at the preparation and insisted that he didn't need any help. I left him to his own devices and reminded myself that we were gonna have to talk privately at first opportunity.

Everyone was ready and I moved over, looking at the guard one more time. He was covered in dripping towels and prison-issue clothes so no one would know he was a hostage, and that'd give him some added protection.

With Stanley and Boots in the lead Frank quickly said, "We keep the guard between us in the middle and no one gets in close to him." Everyone nodded in agreement and started out the door. I grabbed the radio off the desk and moved around Weasel as Frank, then the hostage, filed out through the open door. As I walked out, I pulled my gas mask in place and moved up beside the guard standing in place on the tier.

Ahead of us Stanley had stopped and was pointing across the cellblock. Through the haze and smoke I could barely make out another group moving down the opposite tier. Stanley was saying something to Frank and I stepped in closer to hear. Stanley mumbled through his mask, "They had their hostages blindfolded and tied. We should tie him." He pointed at our guard hostage standing behind us on the tier. I immediately said, "Where's he gonna go . . . what can he do?" I thought Stanley understood why we didn't make it obvious that Diego was a guard. Frank said, "I

don't think it matters now, let's just get him to the front." Stanley muttered something, hesitated, then turned and trudged on down the tier. I followed, shaking my
head and wondering where Stanley's heart was in all this. Will he stand with us or
against us? Then we were at the stairs and I continued following Stanley and Boots
down with Frank and the guard behind me, with Weasel bringing up the rear.

At the bottom I stepped out into the ankle-deep water and noticed for the first time
that it hadn't gotten any deeper. It must be draining off somewhere but I could still hear
water squirting from the broken pipes in the bathroom across from the stairway.

We moved out into the hallway and into the curtain of gray, swirling smoke. It felt
like it was blowing slightly from the direction of the gym. Turning my head to look
up and down the long corridor, I couldn't see anything except the back of Boots, who
was three paces ahead. Looking behind me, I could just make out the ghostly image
of Frank five or six paces back.

Slow and deliberate we filed down the hallway and moved over to the left side
wall. Traversing silently, we'd learned that it was possible to move quietly through the
water by not lifting our feet out of it but kinda sliding our feet along the floor surface with each step. It was a tedious, slow shuffle, but in that blinding smoke it was
an asset to be able to move silently and listen.

The only sound any of us could hear was the rumbling roar that was getting
louder as we moved closer to the gym. And with it the heat was rising at each step.

The hairs on my hands and wrists started to feel prickly and the red-hot ash flew
by my face. Some of it rattled off my rubber mask. The heat rose suddenly hotter and
I felt a rising panic. I knew the fire had broken through the gym wall into the hallway, cutting off our route to the chow hall. I couldn't see flames, but I could see a
red glow ahead.

Suddenly I felt a hand on my back groping, grabbing at my shirt and Frank's
gravel voice saying, "I can't see, my eyes, my eyes. I can't see. Help me brother. I
can't fuckin' see!" I stumbled ahead a couple of steps and turned to see Frank
clutching a handful of my shirt and rubbing his eyes with his other hand. Behind
him the guard held on to his shoulder and Weasel hung onto the guard's back. They
were frantically rubbing their eyes. I hesitated only a moment and kept moving
ahead. I knew Stanley and Boots were at our front and I desperately had to reach
them. I stumbled ahead six or eight paces, feeling along the wall for the opening
and there it was. I immediately turned and almost fell through the doorway into the
chow hall.

The intense blowing heat subsided almost completely and I shuffled away from
the opening to get some distance from flying embers. Frank held on until I stopped.

Smoke filled the room, making everything indiscernible. It seemed thicker and
cloying, like a white out that completely blanks all vision, all sense of direction.

There, with the unseen tables around us, Frank said, "I'll just be a minute. Let me
get this shit out of my eyes." I turned in a complete circle trying to figure out which
way to go. The guard started coughing and Frank hissed at him. "Don't breath too
deep. Just take shallow breaths." I glanced where I thought Weasel should be and said,
"Weasel, can you see?" He coughed and said, "Yeah, a little. But I can see barely anything." At all three of them I said, "Grab on to each other. Come on. We gotta keep

moving." I stuck out my left arm in their direction and felt someone grab it. And we crept ahead in the direction I thought the kitchen would be.

Like four blind mice we moved through the chow hall. Then ahead I heard a faint, muffled voice. "This way . . . come this way." It was Stanley and immediately I yelled into my mask. "Keep talking . . . keep talking!" and I changed direction slightly for the sound of his voice saying, "What, what did you say?" Frank yelled, "Damn it, just keep talking," and he started a round of coughing and gagging.

I groped along from table to table following the sound of Stanley's garbled litany, waving my lead pipe out in front of my like a blind man searching for the curb to the street. His voice got louder and more distinct and there he stood between the two serving lines babbling something about, "If I had a pickle . . ." and when he saw me emerge from the smoke he said, "What happened? I thought you guys were right behind me." I didn't say anything, just stumbled past and through the swinging door into the kitchen.

Amazingly the kitchen was relatively clear of smoke. I jerked the gas mask off my face and breathed clear, fresh air. Someone had turned on all the ceiling exhaust fans and any smoke that gotten in the area had been immediately sucked outside. The whole kitchen was brightly lit from the numerous overhead skylights.

Frank and the rest of our straggling group moved in behind me and then rushed to Boots over by the huge cooking pots and a gushing water faucet. I watched them for a minute as they splashed cold water over their faces and started telling Stanley and Boots about our bit of excitement. Stanley stood at one of the countertops pouring water on his gas mask. When I stepped over closer he said, "There's something in that smoke gettin' in my mask." He poured more water on it. I thought he knew the filters in these military-style masks only last for so long. We didn't have replacement filters or the time to clean the ones in our masks. "We've only got a little ways to go to the front and we can clean the filters later," I said and stepped over to the water faucet for a drink. I'd just dipped my head under for a gulp when I heard the coughing and gagging behind us.

Spinning around I saw the six strangers standing in the kitchen doorway. They noticed us first as they came in and stood by the door coughing and spitting and pulling towels off their faces. Two were obviously hostage guards. They were naked except for the blindfolds, tied together, and pulled into the room. Two of the strangers nodded their heads acknowledging our group facing them. Frank and Diego stood about five paces to my left, Boots and Weasel just to the left of them. Stanley stood to my right at the counter, hunched over and ready to leap if these unknowns made any overt moves. They all stayed by the door eyeing us as we watched them. Frank broke the tension by asking, "You taking them to the front?" indicating the two bent over, naked men coughing. One of the strangers stepped forward and said, "Yeah, that's right. What 'chu guys doing?" He's Chicano but I didn't know him. Frank glanced over at me and said, "We ready?" I immediately said, "Yeah, we're ready," and I turned to Stanley and said to him, "Hey brother, you take the lead again and I'll hang back and watch our rear." Stanley moved sideways, shaking water from his gas mask, still eyeing the strangers. He stepped over to Boots and Weasel, pulled his mask over his face, and pushed through the door into the guards' mess hall. Boots fell in step and followed with Frank and Diego next. I kept watching the strangers and glanced toward the exit. Weasel stood there holding the door, watching me. I quickly moved across the space between us and just before I pulled my mask in place, I pointed at the water spigot and said to the strangers, "There's some fresh water," and followed Weasel through the door.

The room was socked full of smoke and I hurried my pace. Then for a second the smoke seemed to clear and I could see Weasel in front of me. In front of him Frank and Diego were just passing through the hallway door. I dog-trotted up beside Weasel and mumbled, "Come on, let's catch up," and we broke into a run. At the hallway we stumbled and saw the shapes of Frank and Diego moving down the corridor against the far right wall. We continued on to catch up to them.

The smoke wasn't as thick on this side of the fire. It felt like it was moving toward the gym. Probably just a draft pulling air to the gym.

We caught Frank at the control center gates. He was just turning in when a large group materialized from the second gate and surrounded Stanley and Boots. I heard one say, "Where the fuck you guys think you're going?" Stanley just stood there looking at the speaker. Boots turned and looked back at the rest of us. Frank and Diego hesitated and I quickly moved around them to stand beside Stanley. Three of the guys blocking our paths had gas masks on, the other five had towels around their faces. I didn't know or recognize any of them or which side they represented. The speaker said, "I asked you once, where you going?" Stanley said, "We're going to the visiting room," and brought his bar up. One of the guys to the left of the first speaker said, "No one goes past us unless they got hostages." He had a pick-ax handle in his hand, bringing it up higher with each word he mumbled through his mask. Boots at my right shoulder muttered, "Oh God . . . no," and I quickly said, "We heard the message on the radio to bring our hostage to the visiting room." These guys had to be with Felix. One of the speakers said something in Spanish and the one next to him said, "Where's your hostage." He looked from each of us to the other and sarcastically mouthed out, "Which one of you is supposed to be the hostage?" No one moved for a long moment and I knew something had to be said or done to defuse this. These guys were placed here with the explicit purpose to keep the crazies from interfering with the hostage exchange.

Then from behind us Frank said, "This is our hostage!" I saw him out of the corner of my vision moving up beside Stanley on the left, pulling Diego forward by the arm. I kept my attention on the three in gas masks, the leaders of this group, waiting, seeing their reaction. "Why ain't his hands tied? Why's his eyes not covered?" one of them said. Ahh shit . . . they think we're lying. They probably think we're trying to sneak out. Frank shot back with, "We didn't tie him 'cause it wasn't needed. But if that what it takes to get through, I'll tape his hands." He started digging around in his bag and brought out the gray duct tape and immediately wound it around our hostage's hands. Diego just stood there like a trooper, not saying anything. I kept glancing from Frank's quick movements to the reaction of the group around us. They just watched as he finished taping the guard's hands together and pulled the towel down over his eyes. With a flourish, he wound a piece of tape around his head to hold the towel in place and with equal polish he turned on the last speaker of the group and said, "Is that good enough!!?" Frank is ballsy and about half crazy, but the speaker of the other group didn't seem to catch the cheeky words. "Yeah, that's all right. Go ahead," he mumbled through his mask and the entire group stepped to the side. As they passed the speaker he said, "You better be who you say you are. The ones ahead know who the hostages are." We kept filing through without looking back. I stepped in behind Frank with Boots and Weasel bringing up the rear.

In the blackened short hallway we crept along, expecting and waiting for someone to rush out from the burned offices. The smoke had thinned out at eye level and below. Most of it rolled along near the ceiling. I kept peering into each office as we passed them.

Then ahead Stanley hesitated at the visiting room door and looked back at us. Suddenly a familiar voice resounded, "Well come on in . . ." and Stanley disappeared through the doorway. I rushed around Frank and Diego to the door and there sat Bear with a big friendly grin on his face. He sat at the first long visiting table with that same silver-glitter jacket over his shoulders.

I stepped on in through the door and noticed the gun Bear had leveled at my gut. It was one of those breech-loading gas guns, very similar to the M-79 grenade launcher that I had used in Vietnam. It could shoot a variety of shells, but in here I'm sure that it held a tear gas shell. Still though, they're deadly when they explode on impact.

I looked up from the gun to his face and he said, "Where's your hostage?" I immediately pointed over my shoulder behind me saying, "Right back there," and pulled my gas mask off. I saw the recognition in his face and he laid the gun across his lap.

I turned partially to the right and saw Stanley standing against the wall and Frank led Diego in behind me. Bear said, "Take the hostage into the lobby, but leave all your weapons on the table before you go out on the grass." He pointed down the length of the table strewn with an assortment of knives and clubs.

I stepped around Stanley and on past the loaded table looking at the weapons that were left behind by those ahead of us. Maybe the madness is over, maybe so . . . but I'm not ready to throw down anything until I'm sure it's safe to do so. I continued on past the table toward the lobby.

Leading the way out of the visiting room, no one in our group left weapons behind. I passed the overturned pop machine, the wrecked and leaking coffee machine, and around the last turn into the lobby.

The confidence I felt in reaching the lobby was electrifying. And seeing Felix, Lucky, and the five or six others around the lobby doors sent a tremor of relief through my whole core. Hesitating for a moment, I turned to see Frank and Stanley on both sides of our hostage, whisking him along at a near trot. Turning toward the front again, Felix saw us and he waved us on forward. Then I noticed the others standing in the darkened shadows on the far side of the lobby. We were moving through a shaft of brilliant sunlight that reflected in through the lobby doors. Even under this microscope of light and the many eyes watching our progress, it didn't dampen our enthusiasm in reaching our goal.

As we cruised up to the doors, Felix immediately gave instructions to unbind the guard. Then he walked through the lobby doors to the cement stoop beyond. I stood to the side and watched as he waved toward the gun tower and received a responding wave from the two uniformed cops leaning out one of the tower windows. I also noticed the crowd of unarmed convicts milling around on the grass of no-man's land below the gun tower.

Felix came back through saying, "Ready?" and the radio in my pocket squawked and a muffled voice said, "They're sending another hostage out." I jerked it out of my back pocket as I fumbled with the knobs to turn it down. Diego was led past by two of Felix's crew.

They escorted him through the double doors, down the two steps, one on each side as they made their way toward the gate. I could see the two cops in the tower watching the three through binoculars, walking along the sidewalk. They're probably trying to identify him, but I'm sure he doesn't resemble any picture they may have of him.

Diego and his escort continued down the sidewalk, passing the watching convicts on the grass, and when they were about 30 feet from the gate, his escort halted and he continued on to the gate alone. There two suited officials questioned him briefly. When they were satisfied of his preliminary identification, one of the suits raised his arm and the gate rattled open just enough for him to squeeze through. As soon as he reached the other side, the gate slammed shut and eight or ten armed State Police rushed up to surround him.

I continued watching from the lobby doors as he was marched around the small building and out of sight. I let out the breath that I didn't realize I'd been holding.

19   All for Nothing

Stepping back from the lobby doors, I listened as Felix explained to Frank what the negotiations had accomplished. "The Governor sent a message," he said confidently. "He's on his way to the penitentiary and if we'll release all the hostages, he said he'd talk to us." Felix held up the file cards saying, "I'll give these to him personally." He waved the cards around as if they held the answer to all that's been done—as if they were some sort of Holy Grail. I wasn't so sure anymore . . .

Glancing around the room, I tried to find other familiar faces in the darkened shadows. Most were lounging against the wall waiting on the next round of whatever was to come. I didn't recognize but maybe three or four faces of the 20 or more people. All were talking in low whispers, keeping an eye on the vestibule to the visiting room, waiting.

Felix said something about releasing all the guards, but two of those he planned to hold until the Governor arrived. When he said he'd turn over these with the cards, I turned back to hear him say, "We're all being transferred to federal prison."

Stanley got our attention saying, "Who are those guys out on the grass?" I stepped over beside him to see what he was pointing at. I'd noticed them but hadn't paid them much attention. Felix said with irritation, "We found them hiding in Cellblock 5." Stanley pointed and whispered, "There they are, see 'em." I focused in the direction he was pointing his finger and Felix said, "We found that idiot making all those threats." Felix said, "We took their weapons and ran 'em out there where they can't give us any trouble." I glanced over at Stanley and he said, "Do you see 'em?" I nodded slowly at sighting the three guys we'd left for dead in the TV room. There they sat on the grass, holding bloody rags to their heads.

Suddenly the buzzing stopped around the lobby and we spun around to see four convicts pulling two naked hostages into the room on the ends of leash-like ropes. They were the same group that had walked in on us while we were in the kitchen. As they came forward, Stanley and I moved to the side to watch the strange scene with the rest of the silent spectators.

While Felix talked briefly with the four convicts, Frank and Lucky worked at cutting the twine wrapped around the soon-to-be-freed guards' hands. They stood in the glaring shaft of light from the doors, trembling and shaking. When Frank pulled the rag off the eyes of the hostage he worked on, the guard croaked, "I can't feel my hands." He held his hands up, shaking them and trying to focus his eyes on them and on Frank and glancing around at the darkness around him. I tried to see his hands but he kept shaking them. They'd probably been tied for so long that the circulation had been cut off. Frank said to him, "You better tell the medics as soon as you get out the gate." He hunched down shaking, looked around, and shuffled to the door.

The other hostage that Lucky cut loose just stood in place looking straight ahead, not saying anything. Lucky asked him something but he made no response. He acted as if he was in a trance. When Felix came back in from waving at the gun tower, this guard had to be pulled through the lobby doors. We watched as he was led down the sidewalk. When the gate was finally opened for them, two cops from the outside had to come in and pull him through and lead him around the small building to a waiting ambulance. He just followed in a daze.

Stanley and I moved away from the doors. We spotted Boots and Weasel in the shadowed darkness near the lobby wall and meandered over to them. Stanley asked Boots if he'd seen Robert or any of those young Indians in the room. Boots shook his head saying, "I ain't seen them since we split up at Cellhouse 2. They're probably still inside somewhere." Stanley pointed toward the lobby doors and said, "Those three we had that fight with in Dorm F-2 are out there on the grass." We all glanced toward the doors. Nothing else needed to be said. We now knew where that threat was and we'll just have to deal with it when and if it comes to that.

Three more hostages were brought into the lobby. These at least had some clothes on. When they were freed of their bonds and told they could leave, they scurried out through the doors ahead of their escort and broke into a run to the front gate. It would have been humorous if they hadn't been so pitifully frightened.

Suddenly the radios around the room squawked and a vaguely familiar voice spilled out with, "I know who you are . . . you won't get away with what 'chu did to my officers." I glanced at Stanley to see if he'd heard it. He mouthed silently, "Who's that?" I pulled the radio from my pocket and the voice said, "We're gonna get 'chu for what 'chu done. We're gonna get 'chu." I turned the volume up and saw everyone listening to five or six radios in the lobby. Then someone shouted, "Hey, that's Green Eyes. I'd know that voice anywhere." Others around the lobby agreed after hearing more of his homespun verbosity. The threats would rant on until he ran out of breath and his voice rose three or four octaves. It sounded comical and the laughter started breaking all the tension in the room. Green Eyes is one of those middle-aged guards that had started working at the prison 20 years ago. A character on the guard force who strutted around the joint like a banty rooster and thought of himself as a mean, tough, hard-nosed officer—especially when he had five or six other guards behind him. He demanded that everyone call him Lieutenant Marcus, but invariably he's known as Green Eyes—a Chicano with bright, sea-green eyes. He was notorious for doing something silly or irrational, like now. At one point, he stopped talking suddenly, to take a breath no doubt, and Lucky said quickly into his radio, "We'll give up all the hostages . . . if Green Eyes will come in . . ." and peals of laughter rolled louder around the lobby. The radios were silent from then on.

Stanley and I moved around the wall for a better vantage point to see what was going on out through the lobby doors. We could see down the walkway of no-man's land and those convicts on the grass. Out beyond the fence, National Guard and State Police were marching into view, coming toward the gate.

Two more tied hostages came through and were taken out like the others. After they left the lobby, Felix and Lucky turned from the doors and walk slowly through the room, talking to each other in Spanish. They passed us and walked around the corner toward the visiting room and prison center. I kept watching Frank and the others near the doors. They would turn, glancing back in the direction that Felix and Lucky left, and out toward the front again. Something was happening.

Then Felix walked in the lobby again from the visiting room. He moved past us and directly behind him two guards in full uniform shuffled by with their hands cuffed at their back. Moving behind the two guards, Bear still had his silver coat on with a knife drawn in one hand and the gas gun in the other. Lucky walked beside him and as they moved through the lobby, it got suddenly quiet and then the buzzing whispers started again. The guards weren't blindfolded and they rolled their heads back and forth. Their fear was obvious as they tried to see into the darkness of the shadowed room. Someone from across the lobby said angrily, "What the hell they still got their fuckin' pig suits on for?!" Lucky spun in the direction of the voice and said, "Don't you fuckin' worry about it . . ." and followed behind Bear, glaring at everyone on that side of the room. No one else said anything loud enough to be heard distinctly. I could hear the whispered questions of "What's going on?" and "Who are they? Where'd they come from?" The assemblage moved to the front of the lobby and Felix conferred with Bear for a moment, pointing to something out front. Then he pushed through the doors and marched alone down the sidewalk to the gate.

Watching from our vantage point, we could see Felix talking with the suited officials through the gate. Lucky and Bear stood to the side of the doors holding the two guards and watching Felix as if they expected a sign or something.

Frank then stepped away from the lobby doors and vanished into the deeper shadows of the lobby across from us. The room was a blend of obscure shaded darkness on both sides of the lit middle.

Stanley muttered, "Do ya' see that?" and I glanced back toward the front doors. "What is it?" I asked. "See those cops by the base of the tower?" He pointed to a small crowd of black-clad individuals, all were carrying scoped rifles. "Yeah, I see 'em." That's the new force they call S.W.A.T. I've seen 'em on TV. Those look like sniper guns in their hands." As we watched, they deployed along the outside fence line.

Then over at the gate we saw Felix turn away from the suited officials and stride up the walk toward us in the lobby. As he came through the entrance he had a strained, forbidding scowl on his face. He said something to Bear and Lucky and turned on the room and announced to everyone, "The Governor's on the way here and they," he pointed toward the gate, "want us to make the final exchange outside on the grass."

"Move across the sidewalk!!" the bullhorn voice bellowed from outside. The voice boomed again, telling those convicts on the grass to move to the other side of the walkway. Through the doors I could see them coming to their feet.

Felix said, "We're going out . . . and wait on the grass for the Governor . . . don't take any weapons, leave your shit in here." He pointed at the lobby floor and then turned to Lucky telling him something in a rush of Spanish.

I started forward watching Felix and those near the doors, also the figures moving across the sidewalk outside. A few others had gravitated toward the door as Felix began laying out the final surrender. We approached the front lobby watching those outside straggle silently from the right to the left side of the walkway. I tried to locate the three we'd spotted earlier but they had evidently moved further down the left fence line. With the last moving across and out of our view, the space for us was now clear directly under the gun tower.

Lucky stepped to the doors first. He sauntered through and stood out on the concrete stoop, looking around. Then he waved his arm and Bear growled at the guards, "Let's go," pushing them through with the business end of the gas gun. As the guards stepped out, Lucky pointed to the right and guided them down the steps onto the grass with Bear walking behind pointing the gas gun at their back. They moved about halfway between the front fence and the lobby where Lucky stopped, pointed at the ground, and the two guards sat down.

Others around us were dropping their knives and clubs and filing out the exit one and two at a time. Felix moved around the lobby from group to group telling them the same thing, "The Governor's coming to hear our demands. We have the proof to make the changes." Stanley and I stood by the doors checkin' out the first bunch move across the grass and sitting down around Lucky and Bear.

Behind us I heard the clank and rattle of knives and pipes hitting the floor and more people shuffled out of the shadows and passed through the doors. We watched them join the others and Bear squatted down behind the guards. Lucky stood waving his arm for those crossing the grass to come to him. Already there were 10 to 12 guys sitting around him, Bear, and the two guards.

Felix and Frank appeared beside me. Frank said, "You guys going out?" Before I or Stanley could answer, Felix said, "I'm gonna wait on the Governor and give him these," he fanned the file cards out, "and he'll listen to reason. Those two hostages are the last ones and I'll turn them over to him." His lilting words exuded the confidence that appeared to lighten up his face and eyes. He turned, glancing around the darkened room and said, "We've all got to go out. It's the only way to get what we want." Then he stepped past us to the doors, hesitated for a moment and pulled his knife out, dropping it on the floor as he pushed through. We watched him tread down the steps and on toward the gate.

Frank said, "Well, it's over." Drawing his knife, he tossed it against the wall. I started peeling the tape off my hand as Boots and Weasel moved out of the shadows asking, "Are we going out?" Stanley leaned his steel bar against the door frame saying, "We can't stay in here," and our group continued to disarm ourselves.

I detached the pipe from my right hand, laid it on the floor, dropped my gas mask and radio next to the pipe and helped Weasel pull the tape loose from his wrist. Stanley said, "Should I keep this . . . in case there's trouble?" I glanced at the home-made blade he held out and said, "Man, I don't know . . . whatever you think." He looked at me, then at the knife, and said, "Fuck it . . . I'm keepin' it!" and stuck it in his belt and pulled his shirt down over it.

With the decision made to go out, we stood there for a moment looking around and at each other. I spotted a few guys move through the lobby toward the prison cen-ter. They had no intention of giving up yet. Others still held back, unsure of what to do. Finally I said, "Well, it's now or never," and I gingerly stepped through the lobby doors, paused glancing to the left, then right and ambled down the two steps to the sidewalk. There I cut to the right and led the way across the soft grass toward Lucky and Bear.

They still squatted behind the two guards with 25 or 30 guys around them. Other small groups sat and stood around the no-man's land. I moved closer to the bigger group, checking out the ground, looking for a spot to sit down. When I found it, I stopped and felt someone grab my arm.

Stanley held my arm, pulling me away from the large group that had encircled Lucky and Bear and the two hostages. He hissed at me, "Are you crazy? We don't want to be too close to them if there's shootin'. We'd be the first ones shot. Anyone near those guards will be shot." I whipped my head around looking at the forces pointing rifles. Most were aiming in at the larger group around the hostages. "Ahh . . . shit!" I mumbled and followed Stanley around the group. He led the way for about 30 yards and stopped, turned in a circle and sat down facing the fence that was about 20 yards away. As I walked to him he said, "This is far enough. We shouldn't be considered a threat to anyone here."

Our small group settled on the cold, damp grass watching as more and more forces mustered along the outside fence. Already the fence was lined with National Guardsmen facing in with their rifles held at port-arm across their chests. Above us, almost directly over our heads, the tower windows bristled with rifle barrels point-ing down at targets on the grass. Suddenly it didn't seem like a good idea to have come out here.

To our left Felix stood at the gate, talking in an animated conversation with a covey of suited officials. Their words floated over to us, two or three words at a time. He shook a handful of cards and paperwork at the officials. Then his voiced raised, saying, "I'll give up the hostages when the Governor gets here." The whole group of officials just nodded their heads and I could see one talking to Felix as if he didn't want anyone else to hear.

Glancing up at the tower windows, I saw those black-clad S.W.A.T. snipers aim their rifles down at the group around the two hostages. I felt the hairs on the back of my neck start to prickle. Something wasn't quite right.

Then I jerked around as Felix started yelling, "Nooo, that's not the agreement!" And he backed away from the gate. "We're not giving up until the Governor gets here." He added something in Spanish that I didn't understand and he defiantly marched up the sidewalk waving and yelling for everyone to follow him back inside. He kept yelling, "They lied! They lied!"

Everyone on the grass was startled and some moved to stand. When the booming bullhorn voice from the gun tower shrieked, "Everyone lie down—NOW!" everyone froze in place for a moment. I turned to see those National Guardsmen whip their rifles in place at the shoulder—aiming in at all of us. I even heard that familiar metallic snapping of the first shells being chambered into weapons—ready to fire. And that same booming voice, "Anyone that doesn't lie down will be shot!"

I felt a clenching ache grip my gut . . . oh shit . . . they're gonna shoot.

Slowly I turned my head to look back at Felix and saw Frank walking away from us toward Felix and Lucky standing in the middle of the sidewalk arguing. I could hear Felix ranting, "Fuck it! Fuck it!" Surely he's not that stupid. "No . . ." I whispered to myself, watching. He tried to pull away from Lucky. Lucky held on, talking in Spanish to him. Surely the guy knows he'll be shot if he moves any closer to the lobby entrance. And that move will probably get us all shot.

Some of the guys stood at Felix's shouted defiance. They stood planted—looking at him and the forces pointing rifles. Most of the people on the grass moved to stretch out, laying on their stomachs. I slowly turned, moving my legs out and eased facedown on the grass. For a moment I laid my forehead on my folded arms. But I had to see what happened. I had to see it coming.

Glancing toward Felix and Lucky, they continued a dispute in Spanish, struggling toward the lobby steps. Frank kept saying, "No, that won't work . . . no, it's too late . . ." and glancing calmly around at the gate behind him.

I turned to see the suited officials at the gate waving their arms frantically at someone above the gun tower. The words rang clear, "Don't let 'em get to the lobby." It was coming . . . it was coming. I swiveled my head down and tried to flatten myself closer to the ground, preparing for the barrage.

Then from somewhere in the crowd, near the base of the tower, a loud commanding voice shouted above the clamor, "Wait . . . wait! We don't need another Attica." I raised my head slightly to see two new suited individuals stride around the walkway beside the little building and through the crowd of excited cops to stop before the stunned officials around the gate.

They spoke briefly to the suited negotiators and after much head bobbing and pointing in at the compound, one of the new suits stepped to the closed wire gate and announced, "I'm from the Governor's office. He can't be here and I'm here to represent his authority." I raised up further and he said, "Whatever you have for the Governor, I'll take to him personally." He stood there clean, crisp with all that political savvy, staring in at Felix, Lucky, and Frank.

They had spun around watching at the initial outburst about Attica. Lucky had said something to Felix and they exchanged words that I couldn't hear. Then together with Frank, they slowly paced the distance to the gate.

I glanced around in the direction where Bear sat behind the two hostages. He still held the gas gun pointed at their back. The two hostages sat there pale white from the fear and strain. Bear had a fierce, unsmiling expression across his face. He must have known that he was a hair's breath from death with most of those guns pointing at him. All those guys sitting and standing around him looked as if they were just now realizing their proximity made themselves targets as well. But no one moved or made any attempt to move.

Stanley said something beside me and I glanced over at him. He hissed, "I gotta get rid'a this knife." He raised up bringing his left hand out from under him with the knife cuffed and looked like he was gonna throw it. "No, no, no . . ." I whispered and raised up further to block him from any view. "Just push it under the grass into the dirt," I said twisting around to see if any of the cops could see the move. But they weren't paying us any particular attention and when I looked again at Stanley, he'd already stashed the knife.

At the gate Felix listened as the new suit explained his position with the Governor's office. Lucky and Frank stood on each side of Felix. Each of them was firing questions at the man claiming to represent the Governor. He held his hands up saying, "We can end this right now . . . just let those hostages walk out and I'll take the information to the Governor." His voice pleaded and dripped with sincerity. "You have my word on this," he added with equal frankness.

Felix held the cards and papers in both hands saying something about their importance and proof. I couldn't hear it all. Then he turned to Lucky and said, "All right. Let 'em go!" All three turned, waving at Bear to bring the hostages forward.

It's working . . . it's working . . . they're gonna end it. I turned to watch Bear stand and the two other guys helped the guards awkwardly to their feet. Everyone watched silently as the guards and Bear walked slowly across the grass toward the gate.

As they lumbered up to Lucky's side, the suited aide said, "I'll take that information now and you men will have to step back." Felix handed the cards and papers through the links in the gate. The aide accepted them without a glance.

I noticed more National Guard and State Police lining up behind the aide and other onlooking suited officials. They held their rifles at port-arm with the barrels pointing skyward. All of them wore helmets with plastic shields covering their faces. It wasn't too difficult to realize where they were coming when the gate opened.

Felix, Lucky, and Frank moved around the two guards and stepped off the sidewalk to the right. Bear laid the gas gun at the feet of the two guards and he too moved to the side with the others.

It was over. It was finally over but I didn't feel any relief in knowing this. One part is over and now another begins . . .

Then that voice boomed again, "Lay down with your hands out!" I stretched my arms out on each side of my head and laid my head against my arm, squeezing my eyes shut.

When I heard the gate rattle and squeak open, I raised my head in time to see the two hostages shuffle out and two lines of National Guardsmen trot in past them. I watched as rank after rank of troops and police poured through the wide-open gate.

Just behind the moving entering force I could see the suited officials shaking each other's hands. The Governor's aide stood leisurely talking beside Deputy Warden Florez. The rumbling of running feet prevented hearing their conversation and I never could read lips. But they all looked pleased at the outcome. Then the Governor's aide handed the cards and papers to the Deputy Warden—the one and same Deputy Warden whose name appeared on most of those cards—and walked away.

I let my head drop on the grass between my arms. It had been a futile attempt at nothing . . . all for nothing.

A helicopter flew overhead, drowning out all other noise and thought.

Author's Note

The incidents described in this book and those 36 hours in 1980 have haunted this writer to the point that something had to be said about it. For the obvious reasons, all names of the living had to be changed, but I'm sure for those who were there and survived the riot, they know and remember these individuals.

Through a tragedy of errors, the officials at the prison ignored the rumors of an impending takeover and riot. Those same officials believed they had effectively intimidated and demoralized the prisoners to the point that none would have the courage to rebel. And even though the rumors had been circulating through the prisons for months before February 2, 1980, the rumors were laughed off and it was business as usual. But, it should be noted, there was nothing the officials could have done to prevent this takeover. The stage had been set long before the rumors began. Prisons are full of routine and mundane regularity where prisoners can wait for the perfect moment that a guard is lax in judgment or not paying attention.

The group of guards and officials who perfected and perpetuated the ongoing fear and hatred before the riot were eventually identified. The months of investigation after the riot by the Attorney General concluded with removing the deputy warden, head of security and other middle-management prison officials. The Attorney General's report placed the primary blame for the riot on mismanagement of the prison and years of corruption.

Felix, Lucky, Bear, Frank, and many others were charged in the investigation for leadership in the riot. They were all shipped to federal prison facilities. I don't know what became of these individuals. Stanley, Weasel, and Boots were eventually paroled or released. I was able to maintain contact with Stanley for a short while, but as with most prison friendships, we lost contact with and track of each other. Attempts were made to contact Captain Francisco Vasquez, but at the time he was confined to a hospital bed and unable to remember anything of the riot. Donald V. Diego, the burned guard, recovered from his injuries. Since the riot, I have been in contact with Diego. He is doing well and running his own construction business.

Of the numerous dead—independent investigators confirmed that 33 prisoners perished in the riot. An additional prisoner died several months later of his wounds. A team of forensic experts found only three bodies in the burned-out gym, so investigators dispute that bodies were taken to the gym and burned. I do not know how many prisoners were murdered or how many died from overdosing on drugs. But it should be made clear as to why so many were killed. Most of those murdered were thought to be or in fact were informers. In prison, an informer or rat is the most loathed and hated by prisoners. The police use informers to set up and catch criminals. The courts use informers to prosecute their criminal cases, and guards and prison officials use informers to snitch on other prisoners. It shouldn't be surprising that these individuals were the center of attention and retribution once the prison was wide open and without restraint. What was unique in this case is the "snitch game" the officials used to control prisoners.

The hate that permeated this prison was not unique. In most prisons across this country, inmates exceed the capacity by two to three times that for which they were designed. In most American prisons, there are guards and officials who believe that it's part of their job to make those confined as miserable as possible. These guards and officials routinely place the lives of those confined and those who work in these facilities in danger. The spark to light the madness is ahead for all these prisons. The only thing that has changed is the prisoners' attitudes. The prison takeovers and riots of the future won't be to negotiate change or to improve the conditions of those confined. The prisoners of today know this is an exercise in futility. The riots and takeovers of the future will be for one purpose only—REVENGE.

In understanding the events of this story, read it not with the intentions to ask why these horrendous events could have happened in the past. But understand it is still happening and will continue until society realizes that the whole idea of locking a person in a box to repent is a dismal failure. The entire concept of sentencing a person to reform/rehabilitate has not worked and will not work with the present antiquated justice system on which our society relies. When warehousing and abusing a person passes the point that it insults the good senses of what is just and moral, then when that individual is released into society again, he has only learned a deeper hatred and disrespect for society and the laws that have abused him.

PART III

Epilogue: The Times They *Aren't* A-Changing

The observations, narrative, and revelations of this book are not only difficult to read, but even more difficult to assimilate into any civilized notion of what it means to be a human being. How can human beings set each other on fire? Put a torch on another's testicles? Shove a broom up another man's rectum and force him to walk? How can the author describe such horror as though he were merely describing the plays of a football game? Endless questions set our minds reeling and tempt us to rationalize that "those people" are not like "us"; that it's a good thing we have prisons for such vicious brutes.

Yet every human being described in this book, whether attacker or victim (or guard), was once a sweet little baby, an innocent child who wanted nothing more than a kind word, a soft smile, proper nourishment, and guidance—the basics of a good life on Earth. The insanely vicious violence documented in this book—and which unfortunately is encountered in many other institutions as well—is not natural or instinctive; it is a response. It may be a spontaneous response or a learned one or both. But it is a response nonetheless. The Santa Fe riot itself was a long-brewing response, just as was the riot at Attica years earlier. The question is: Can we look honestly at the facts that led to such a horrific response, and change as many of these factors as we can?

---

*   Bo Lozoff and his wife, Sita, are directors of the Human Kindness Foundation in Durham, NC. Bo has led spiritual workshops in more than 500 prisons worldwide since 1973, teaching "the profoundest common sense" of the world's greatest religious and philosophical traditions, and many meditative practices for personal and planetary transformation. Bo's first book, *We're All Doing Time*, now in its eighth printing in several languages, has been lauded by prison staff and prisoners alike as one of the most helpful books ever written for *true* self-improvement and rehabilitation—which in Bo's and Sita's view revolve squarely around unselfishness and compassion for all beings. Bo's follow-up to that book, *Inner Corrections: Finding Peace and Peacemaking,* co-authored by Michael Braswell, provides a guide for finding peace within in order to live more peacefully and noncriminally in the world. The Lozoffs have been cited for numerous humanitarian awards, including, in 1994, the prestigious Temple Award for Creative Altruism. Their sincerity and commitment have earned the respect of tens of thousands of prisoners and ex-offenders around the world who feel inspired to follow a similar path of joyfully caring about others.

151

Obviously, the sweet little babies mentioned above were not pure and sweet by the time they entered prison. Many factors polluted their behavior and attitudes in infancy, early childhood, and adolescence, and are beyond the scope of this book except as a general reminder that a successful society must cherish and educate its children. But it would be a grave error to assume that the horrific violence detailed in this volume had more to do with prior influences than the influence of the prison itself. At the time of their admission into prison, the vast majority of prison inmates are no more prone to such incredible brutality than any reader of this book.

Most new inmates are scared to death and just want to get out of prison alive. Their increasing capacity for violence during their incarceration is a direct response to factors which are very much under our control: The profoundly negative tone of our prisons, the dominant note of anger expressed toward inmates throughout the day by officials, the lack of opportunities to learn responsibility, decency, altruism, and the lack of safety from predators in the prison population.

In short, we place people who are mostly confused, dysfunctional, and selfish into a hellacious environment that turns their confusion into despair, their dysfunctions into sociopathy, and their selfishness into an obsessive struggle for sheer survival. We cannot be surprised at the occasional Santa Fe. To the contrary, I am always surprised there are not many more such riots.

Worse yet, our children are picking up the message of the times—from the way we speak about criminals, the way we cheer over executions, the way we celebrate the return of chain gangs—that it is acceptable to humiliate or brutalize people who have wronged us. The problem is, we cannot control our childrens' perception of "appropriate" targets. The current generation of American adolescents is surpassing all past records for homicide, suicide, and even patricide and matricide. I have witnessed interviews with 11-year-olds who can describe sticking an icepick precisely between the ribs of their victim in order to puncture the heart, as dispassionately as though they were discussing the way to assemble a model airplane. Such dispassion is not natural; it is learned.

So, I am not suggesting modest changes or innovative programs within our dominant prison model. I am pointing out that the most fundamental assumptions we make about imprisonment need to be changed. Our model of retributive justice, of harsh and angry punishment, is making things worse rather than better. This is clear; it is not a close call. It is an urgent priority for our civilization to explore models of justice that are restorative rather than retributive, that heal rather than harm. We need to set aside our infantile tough-on-crime political rhetoric, take a deep breath, step back, and notice how terrible a failure such a system has been. We are not soft on crime, we have not *been* soft on crime. We are extremely tough on crime; we routinely *ruin* people's lives rather than help them to change. We create and endorse the conditions that can lead ordinary human beings to behave in the ways described in this book.

We now imprison millions instead of thousands. The vast majority of those millions will one day be released and walk among us. It is mere sanity to want them to be happier, compassionate, and more capable human beings instead of damaged time bombs waiting to go off. To accomplish this, we need a more compassionate view and the courage to fly in the face of contemporary political sloganeering. We need the foresight to trash our current model rather than improve it.

It can't happen overnight, but our view can indeed change right from the start. When our children do wrong, we don't hate them for the rest of their lives. We don't place them in situations in which they will be raped and battered. We do whatever we can to get them to see what they did wrong, and deepen their values so they become the decent human beings we know they are capable of becoming. We must now have similar faith in other people's children who do wrong, too. A justice system must have at its core a solid belief in human goodness and redemption. Otherwise there will always be another Santa Fe riot just around the corner.